Bring Science Alive! Grade 3

Unit 4

Life Cycles and Traits

Science Journal

TCi™

Unit 4

Life Cycles and Traits

As a science writer for Science Monthly, you've been assigned a feature on Ecuadorian wildlife. Investigate traits of different organisms and tell us your findings.

Engineering

Anchoring Phenomenon

Think about this unit's **Anchoring Phenomenon**: *These two frogs look the same, but only one of them is poisonous!* Complete the chart.

- List what you **know** about this unit's phenomenon.
- Write questions you **wonder** about this phenomenon.

Know	Wonder

Unit Checkpoints

As you complete each lesson, look for this icon ☑ and return to record what you've learned in the lesson.

Lesson	What I Learned
1 Why Do Offspring Look Similar to Their Parents?	
2 How Does the Environment Affect Traits?	
3 How Are Traits Affected by Both Inheritance and the Environment?	
4 Why Do Some Members of a Species Survive and Not Others?	
5 What Are the Life Cycles of Plants?	
6 What Are the Life Cycles of Animals with Backbones?	
7 What Are the Life Cycles of Animals Without Backbones?	

Using what you learned in this unit, explain the unit's **Anchoring Phenomenon**:
These two frogs look the same, but only one of them is poisonous!

Claim	
Evidence	
Reasoning	

Lesson 1
Why Do Offspring Look Similar to Their Parents?

Observing Phenomena

Discuss: Have you ever seen a baby animal next to its parents? Did they look similar?

Observe this phenomenon: *Baby animals look like their parents, but not like the parents of other types of animals.*

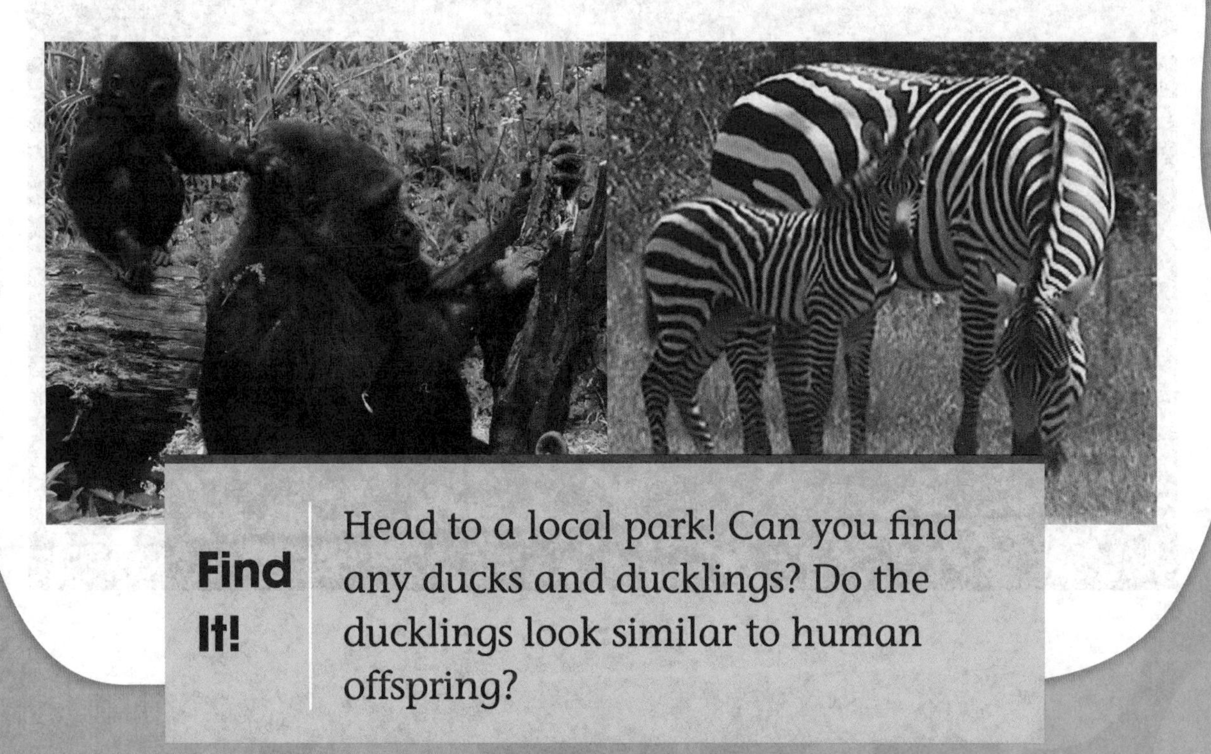

Find It! Head to a local park! Can you find any ducks and ducklings? Do the ducklings look similar to human offspring?

Think of what you already know about how offspring look like their parents. Write questions you have.

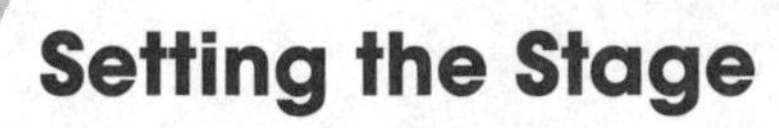

Setting the Stage

In this investigation, you will sort cards to match parents with their offspring.

Sorting Offspring

Answer the following questions based on the visual data that you have examined during the investigation.

a) What are some of the ways you can match offspring to their parents?

b) Do offspring always look the same as their parents? How do they, or how do they not?

Vocabulary

Match the term to the correct definition.

Word Bank

inherited trait   offspring   species   trait

____________________ A group of living things of the same kind.

____________________ A characteristic that a living thing has.

____________________ The young organisms that result when adult organisms reproduce.

____________________ A characteristic passed from a parent to its offspring.

My Science Concepts

Reflect on your understanding. Draw an X along each line.

When observing data about traits, you can look for similarities and differences in the ways organisms look and behave. Organisms of the same species will share more similar traits with each other than they will with a different species.

still learning **know it**

Even within the same species, there is much variation in traits. For example, although most dogs have fur, they will not all have the same color or thickness of fur. They do not usually look identical because they had different parents. Many traits are passed onto their offspring, but offspring can be different from their parents because some of the offspring's traits are not inherited.

still learning **know it**

1. Different Animal and Plant Species Exist

You know that goldfish and lions are different. They look and act differently. That is because goldfish and lions are different *species*.

A **species** is a group of living things of the same kind. Members of an animal species produce young of the same species. For example, there are many different crab species. Coconut crabs and flower crabs are different crab species. Each crab species produces young of the same species. Coconut crabs produce young coconut crabs. Flower crabs produce young flower crabs.

These crabs are all different species. There are many different species of crab, and they all produce young of their same species.

Coconut crab

Flower crab

Japanese spider crab

There are three images of each of these species in the puzzle below: blue crab, snowshoe hare, eastern bluebird, Joshua tree, golden poppy, and sugar maple tree.

Find each species. Circle the group of three images. Then write the name of the species next to the group. One has been done for you.

2. Species Have Traits and Produce Offspring

What is a goat like? What about a fish? Do fish and goats look and act the same? Goats have fur and eat grass. Fish have fins and swim in water. They have different *traits*.

Traits are characteristics that living things have. Different species have different traits. For example, different bird species have feathers with different color patterns. Northern cardinals have many red feathers. Blue jays have blue, white, and black feathers. Brown pelicans have gray, white, and brown feathers.

All species also make more members of their own species called **offspring**. For example, baby white-tailed deer are offspring of adult white-tailed deer. You are offspring of adult humans. Plants also produce offspring. For example, young sugar maple trees are offspring of adult sugar maple trees.

Feather color is a trait. The northern cardinal on the left will have offspring with red feathers. The blue jay's offspring will have its blue, white, and black feathers.

Finish the sentences below. Use the plants and animals in the images as evidence. *Hint: Use the species name in your answers.*

Birds

Emperor penguin

Blue-and-gold macaw

Flowers

Rose of Sharon

Black-eyed Susan

Fruit Trees

Orange tree

Sweet cherry

Characteristics that living things have are called traits. Different bird species have different traits. For example, an emperor penguin has a long, straight beak and a blue-and-gold macaw has a . . .

Different flower species have different traits. For example, . . .

Different fruit tree species have different traits. For example, . . .

This goat kid inherited some of its traits from its parents. Fur color is an inherited trait.

3. Animals and Plants Pass On Traits

At a petting zoo, you may have seen baby goats and their mothers. In what ways do baby goats look like their mothers? What color is their fur?

A characteristic passed by a parent to its offspring is an **inherited trait**. Fur color in goats is an inherited trait. Beak shape and feather color in birds are inherited traits. Different species look different because they have different inherited traits.

Plants also pass on inherited traits to their offspring. A pine tree has needle-shaped leaves. Offspring of that pine tree will have similar leaves. Having needle-shaped leaves is an inherited trait.

Another common inherited trait in plants is how tall a plant can grow. A hollyhock plant can grow to be over 6 m (almost 20 ft). Offspring of that hollyhock plant can also grow to be that tall.

Describe what an inherited trait is. Then find and label one example of an inherited trait in each image.

4. Offspring Are Similar to Their Parents

Think of a mother duck and her ducklings. What similar traits do you think they might share?

A mother duck may look a bit different from her ducklings. But most of the ducklings' traits are similar to their parents. When the ducklings become adults, they will be even more similar to their parents'. The mother duck and her ducklings all have two legs and webbed feet. They all walk and swim the same way.

Many human traits are inherited. For example, this child has inherited her eye color from her mother.

Organisms *inherit*, or receive, traits from their parents. An organism is any living thing, like a dog or a tulip. Most humans inherit traits such as having two legs and being able to walk. Humans have a mixture of traits from both of their parents. They may have inherited their mother's hair color and nose shape. They may have also inherited their father's eye color and mouth shape.

Other animals also inherit traits from their parents. A bat inherits its fur color and ability to fly. It also inherits ears that can hear high-pitched sounds. A goldfish inherits its scale color and fin shape from its parents. It also inherits gills it uses to breathe in water. Spiders that spin webs produce offspring that spin webs. Spiders that hunt for food on the ground produce offspring that do the same. A dog may inherit its mother's coat color but get the length of its fur from its father.

Plants also inherit traits from their parents. An oak tree inherits its branching pattern and basic leaf shape from its parents. It will also produce acorns like its parents do.

Animals inherit traits from their parents. This spider's offspring will also spin webs like their parent does.

Look at this oak tree and its offspring.

Why are offspring similar to their parents? As part of your answer, refer to one specific detail from the text and one detail from these images.

5. Offspring Can Be Different from Their Parents

You have learned that puppies in a group often do not look exactly like one another. Some may have different fur colors. One may be black, while two are brown, and another is spotted.

Animals of a species can have traits that are not the same as their parents'. A goat has hooves and fur like its parents. But it may have horns that are a different length from its parents'. It may also have a broken horn, unlike its parents. Some traits are inherited from parents. Some are not.

Plants of a species can also have traits that are not the same as their parents'. Healthy common daisy plants have stems, leaves, and white petals. But some common daisy offspring may have stems that are taller than their parents'. Some may have petals that are thinner or wider. Stem height and petal width are traits that can be different between offspring and their parents.

Even though offspring inherit many traits from their parents, they do not look exactly like one another. These puppies look slightly different from their parents and from each other.

Animal offspring usually do not look exactly like their parents. What evidence can you find in this diagram to support this claim? Write a paragraph below. Make sure to include the following terms: trait, color, offspring, parents, spots, and inherited trait.

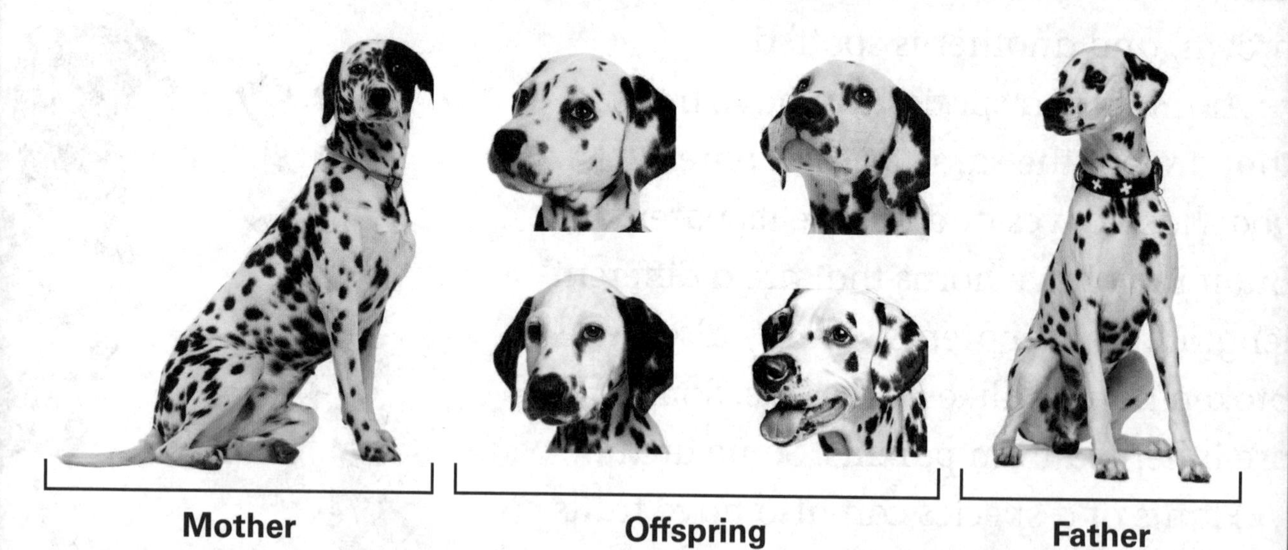

Show What You Know

Carefully observe these two images. They are parents.

a) Which of these is the offspring of the parents above? Circle it.

b) Explain how you predicted which image is the offspring. Use these terms in your answer: species, trait, and inherited.

c) List two traits you think the offspring inherited from its parents.

d) Explain one trait the offpsring has that varies from its parents'.

Making Sense of the Phenomenon

Let's revisit the phenomenon: *Baby animals look like their parents, but not like the parents of other types of animals.*

Think about:

- How are offspring from different types of animals different from each other?
- How are offspring similar to their parents?

Use your findings from the investigation to answer this question: *Why does a baby zebra look more like an adult zebra than an adult gorilla?*

Claim	
Evidence	
Reasoning	

☑ Go back to page 4 and fill out the unit checkpoint for this lesson.

NOTES

Lesson 2

How Does the Environment Affect Traits?

Observing Phenomena

Discuss: Have you ever seen a group of plants that was dead? What are some reasons they could have died?

Observe this phenomenon: *Plants will die if they don't have enough water.*

See It!

In the summer, most trees have green leaves. But what happens to many trees' leaves in the fall and winter? Why do you think this change occurs?

Think of what you already know about the reasons why the leaves of plants and trees can change colors. Write questions you have.

Finding Evidence

For each organism identified in the image,

- choose one of its traits. You can choose a physical characteristic or behavior. Write it under **Trait**.
- describe a way the environment can affect this trait. Write this under **Cause**.
- explain how the trait was changed. Write this under **Effect**.

The first example has been provided for you.

Organism	Trait	Cause (in the environment)	Effect (on the trait)
Boy	Ability to throw.	He watched other people throwing and started practicing how to throw.	He learned how to throw. He can throw the stick high and far.
Dog			
Reeds			

For each organism identified in the image,

- choose one of its traits. You can choose a physical characteristic or behavior. Write it under **Trait**.
- describe a way the environment can affect this trait. Write this under **Cause**.
- explain how the trait was changed. Write this under **Effect**.

Organism	Trait	Cause (in the environment)	Effect (on the trait)
Bushes			
Herder			
Goat			

For each organism identified in the image,

- choose one of its traits. Write it under **Trait**.
- describe a way the environment can affect this trait. Write this under **Cause**.
- explain how the trait was changed. Write this under **Effect**.

Organism	Trait	Cause (in the environment)	Effect (on the trait)
Palms			
Diver			
Fish			

Now let's help an organism find food or shelter! Follow the engineering process with your class.

Vocabulary

Match the word to the correct definition.

Word Bank

learned behavior | environment

_________________________ A trait an organism learns over its lifetime.

_________________________ All the living and nonliving things that surround an organism.

My Science Concepts

Reflect on your understanding. Draw an X along each line.

An organism can gain or lose traits during its lifetime. A plant might turn from green to brown. A human might get taller and stronger.

still learning •———•———•———•———• **know it**

The environment affects an organism's traits. For example, if a plant doesn't get enough water, it may wilt and turn brown. If an animal gets in a fight with another animal, it may get a scar.

still learning •———•———•———•———• **know it**

A learned behavior is a trait that an organism is not born knowing. It learns from its environment and changes its behavior. An animal may learn to avoid bad-tasting plants. A human may learn how to ride a bike.

still learning •———•———•———•———• **know it**

1. Some Traits Are Not Passed to Offspring

Have you ever seen a small, stunted plant? It may have grown that way because it did not get enough water. Or maybe it did not get enough sunlight. The environment caused that plant to have those traits.

An organism can gain or lose traits in its lifetime. Some traits are caused by the *environment* and are not passed on from parents. The **environment** is all the living and nonliving things that surround an organism. A tree may have holes and markings on its trunk because woodpeckers drilled into it. The woodpeckers are part of the tree's environment. Flamingoes are birds with pinkish coloring. The chicks are not this color when they hatch. They get their color from the food they eat. The food they eat is part of their environment.

Flamingoes are not brightly colored when they hatch. They get that trait from the food they eat in their environment.

The table below describes four ways the environment might affect an organism's traits.

Fill in the blanks by placing the following terms in their correct location: **trait, night, winter, coat, tree, close, blow up,** and **prey.**

Environmental Cause	Effect on Organism's Trait	Image
________ falls on a mountain lake.	White tulips ________ their petals at night, to survive the cold night air.	
A hungry woodpecker looks for insects in the bark of a ________.	The holes on a tree trunk are a ________ caused by woodpeckers.	
A cold, harsh ________ lasts for many months.	The thick, warm ________ of grey wolves is a trait that helps them survive the long winter months.	
A predator swims after its ________.	Puffer fish ________ to many times their size to fool predators.	

2. Traits Can Change in Animals

Have you ever told a dog to sit or roll over? Dogs are not born knowing how to do that.

The things an animal does are traits. Some of those traits are learned. A **learned behavior** is a trait that an organism learns during its lifetime. Animals can learn new behaviors. Some owls may learn to hunt new types of prey. A wolf that lost a limb may learn to walk on three legs. An animal may eat a plant that tastes bad. It will learn not to eat that plant again. Animals learn from their environments.

Some traits change because of something that happened in the animal's environment. A hamster that is overfed can gain weight. It may not be able to run as fast. A lion that has been in a fight may get scratched or clawed. Its injuries will heal, but its skin may be scarred. These scars are traits.

Some organisms learn behaviors from their environment. Young foxes learn how to hunt by watching their parents.

1) Explain how some animals learn traits. Give two examples.

2) Choose one of the animals and traits above. Complete the flowchart by drawing what happened in the animal's environment that caused this trait (learned behavior).

Animal: ____________________

Trait (learned behavior): ____________________________________

Cause (what happens in the environment)		Effect (how the trait changes)
	→	

3. Traits Can Change in Humans

Suppose you fall off your bike and scrape your knee. After your knee heals, a scar forms. A scar is a new trait.

People's traits are affected by their environment. If people do not eat enough food, they can lose weight. If a child's environment does not have nutritious food, they may not grow very tall.

Like other animals, some traits you have are learned. When you were born, you did not know how to tie your shoes. You learned to tie your shoes when you were older. A few years later, you may have also learned how to ride a bike. These learned behaviors are traits.

Writing is a learned behavior. This child did not know how to write when he was born.

Describe one trait you have learned. How did you learn it? Did you know how to do it when you were born? Do you think you will always be able to do this behavior?

4. Traits Can Change in Plants

Have you ever tried to grow flowers or other plants? What if the plant's environment has too much sunshine? Or not enough sunshine?

The environment can change some traits in plants, too. Plants that get dried out from too much sunshine may turn brown. Plants that do not receive enough sunshine may change color. A plant's color is a trait that can change. The environment can change a plant's color.

Another trait that can change in plants is height. If a plant's environment has enough water and sunshine, that plant may grow very tall. If a plant's environment does not have the right amount of water or sunshine, that plant may not grow very tall. The environment can change a plant's height.

This plant's environment has plenty of water and sunshine. Its environment is helping the plant grow tall.

Draw two plants, and label how the environment has changed their traits.

Show What You Know

Describe three pieces of evidence that support the claim below. Make sure to read each hint and to record your source for each piece of evidence.

Claim: Traits can be influenced by the environment.

Evidence #1

Source:

Hint #1: Find and quote evidence from the text.

Evidence #2

Source:

Hint #2: Find a piece of evidence from your investigation notes.

Evidence #3

Source:

Hint #3: Come up with evidence based on your own observations of the world around you.

Making Sense of the Phenomenon

Let's revisit the phenomenon: *Plants will die if they don't have enough water.*

Think about:

- Do you think this plant's offspring will also need water to survive?
- How would watering these plants change their traits?

Use your findings from the investigation to answer this question: *How did the environment change these plants' physical traits?*

Claim	
Evidence	
Reasoning	

☑ Go back to page 4 and fill out the unit checkpoint for this lesson.

NOTES

Lesson 3

How Are Traits Affected by Both Inheritance and the Environment?

Observing Phenomena

Discuss: Have you ever seen a tree in the winter with no leaves? Do some trees look different in the summer than they do in the winter?

Observe this phenomenon: *By wintertime, some trees have lost all their leaves while some stay green all year.*

See It! Do the trees you see still have leaves?

Think of what you already know about when many trees tend to lose their leaves. Write questions you have.

Reviewing Inheritance and Environment

Fill in the blanks to complete each sentence.

Word Bank

genes	environment	species
offspring	inherited	traits

A __________________________ is a group of living things of the same kind. Parents produce __________________________ of the same kind. Young plants and animals often share __________________________ , or characteristics, with their parents. They might have a fur color similar to their parents' or have leaves that are shaped in a similar way. This is because __________________________ information is passed from parents to their young through __________________________ . However, organisms of the same kind don't look identical! And organisms can gain or lose traits over their lifetimes. This is because some traits are not passed on from parents. These traits are caused by the __________________________ , which is all the living and nonliving things that surround an organism.

Analyzing Flowcharts

Follow these steps:

- Get a copy of *Handout: Puzzle Pieces*. Cut out the pieces.
- Figure out where the images and labels should be placed on the flowchart.
- Carefully examine the flowchart.
- Discuss the question below. Be prepared to share your answer with the class.

How was each offspring's final appearance affected by its inheritance and its environment?

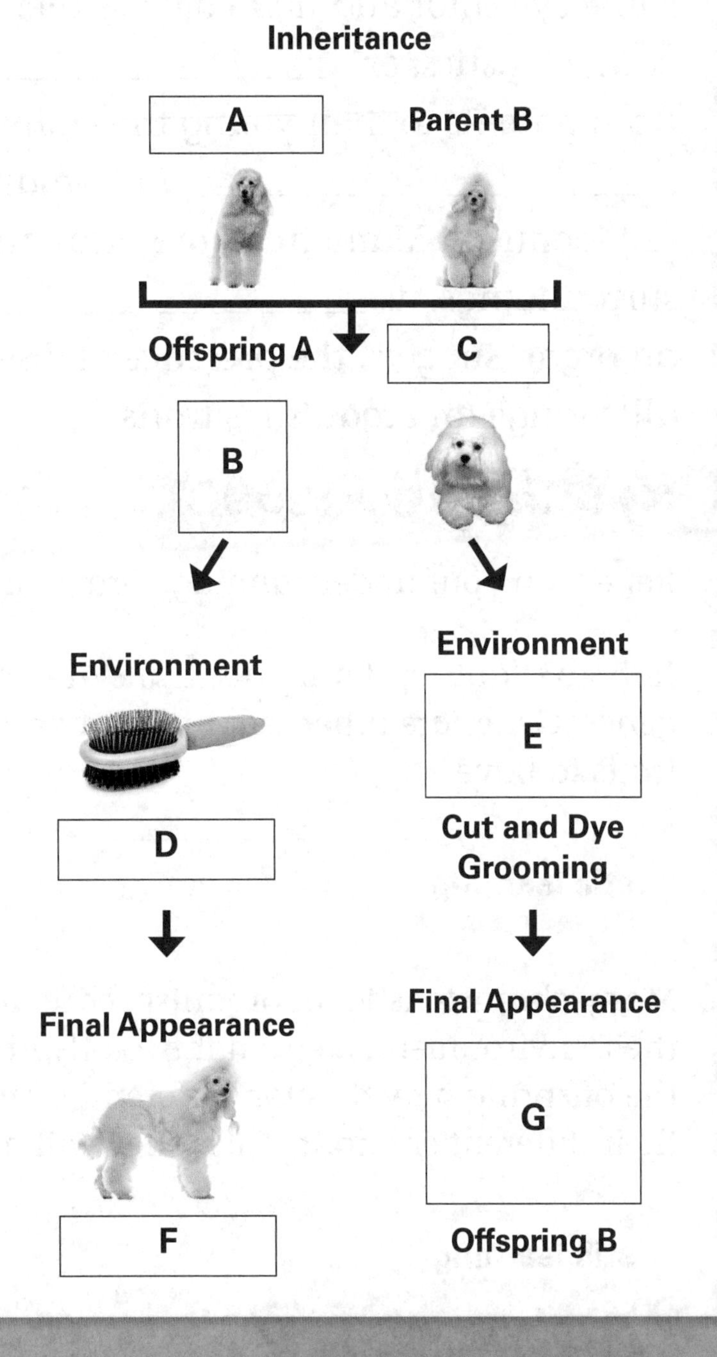

Vocabulary

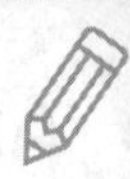

Fill in the blanks to complete each sentence.

Word Bank

genes traits offspring environment

____________________ share many characteristics with their parents. For example, they might have the same eye color and hair color as their parents. These characteristics, or ____________________ , are passed from parents to their young through inherited information in ____________________. But organisms of the same species are not identical! Many traits are also influenced by an organism's surroundings, its ____________________. The amount of food an organism gets, the presence of diseases, and other factors can all change an organism's traits.

My Science Concepts

Reflect on your understanding. Draw an X along each line.

In both plants and animals, traits are passed on to offspring through genes. Genes are inherited information that tell offspring's bodies what traits to have.

still learning **know it**

Many characteristics of organisms are affected by both their genes and their environment. So even if two offspring got the exact same genes, the offspring may develop differently. Their traits will be affected by their different environments. They will not be exactly the same.

still learning **know it**

1. Plants Inherit Genes

You have already learned that some traits can be inherited. Think of an adult rose plant. It has many big, pink flowers. Now think of its offspring, a baby rose plant. Does that baby plant have big, pink flowers? No, it does not. Do you think that baby plant will have flowers when it grows up?

Inherited traits are passed on through *genes*. **Genes** are inherited information that tells offspring what traits to have. That adult rose plant passed on genes to its offspring. Those genes tell the baby plant how to grow flowers when it is older. The baby plant does not have flowers when it sprouts. It grows them when it is older. But the flowers are still an inherited trait. The genes passed to a baby plant from its parents tell the plant what kind of flowers to grow and when.

This baby rose plant has inherited genes to grow flowers. The flowers are an inherited trait.

Draw and label a diagram showing that a parent plant passes on inherited traits to its offspring as genes.

Hint: Traits might include petal color, height, leaf shape, and flower shape.

2. Plant Inheritance and the Environment

Think of a baby rose plant again. It has inherited genes to grow big, pink flowers. Does that mean it will always grow big, pink flowers in its lifetime? No, it does not.

Many traits of plants are affected by both inheritance and the environment. For instance, the rose plant has inherited genes to grow big, pink flowers when it is older. But what if the plant gets a disease from another plant in its environment? The diseased rose plant may only grow brown, unhealthy flowers. The rose plant's flowers are a trait that was affected by inheritance and the plant's environment.

Another baby rose plant may also inherit genes to grow big, pink flowers. If its environment does not have the disease, then the rose plant will be healthy. It will grow big, pink flowers. This rose plant has a different trait because its environment is different.

These plants inherited the same genes to make big, pink flowers. But the environment of the plant on the bottom gave it a disease. That made it grow unhealthy flowers instead.

How are a plant's traits affected by a combination of genes and environmental effects? Use at least one of the examples below and the following terms in your answer: **inherited genes, environmental effect,** and **trait**.

Examples:
- a red rose that does not get enough water
- a mulberry leaf that is eaten by a silkworm
- a stalk of grass frozen by a long winter

3. Animals Inherit Genes

Have you ever seen a newborn baby bird? Most baby birds do not have feathers. But most adult birds do! How does a baby bird's body know to grow feathers as it gets older?

Like plants, animals inherit traits that are passed on as genes. For instance, baby birds may not have feathers when they are born. They grow feathers when they are older. Baby birds inherit genes to grow feathers from their parents. Their feathers are an inherited trait.

Another example is a frog's legs. Tadpoles do not have legs when they are born. They grow legs as they grow older and become adults. Tadpoles inherit genes from their parents to grow legs. So, their legs are an inherited trait.

These tadpoles hatched with no legs. But they inherited genes from their parents to grow legs when they are older.

Put two circles on each image. One circle should show a trait in the baby. The other circle should show how that trait will change when the baby grows up. Then write a caption explaining why the trait will change. Use the term **inherit** in your answer.

4. Animal Inheritance and the Environment

What is some inherited information that animals can have? Can you think of how the environment might affect them?

Like plants, many traits of animals are affected by inheritance and the environment. One trait that can be affected is size. For instance, a wild piglet may inherit genes that tell it to grow to 50 kg (110 lb). If the piglet does not eat very much food, it may only grow to 30 kg (66 lb). Another wild piglet may inherit genes to grow to 30 kg. If the piglet eats enough food and water, it may grow to 30 kg, too. Both pigs are 30 kg, but they grew up in different environments and inherited different genes. Their size is a trait that is affected by both inheritance and the environment.

These two pigs grew up to be the same size. But they may have inherited different genes and grown up in different environments.

Carefully review the flowchart below. Notice that each of the pigs inherited the same genes for gaining weight.

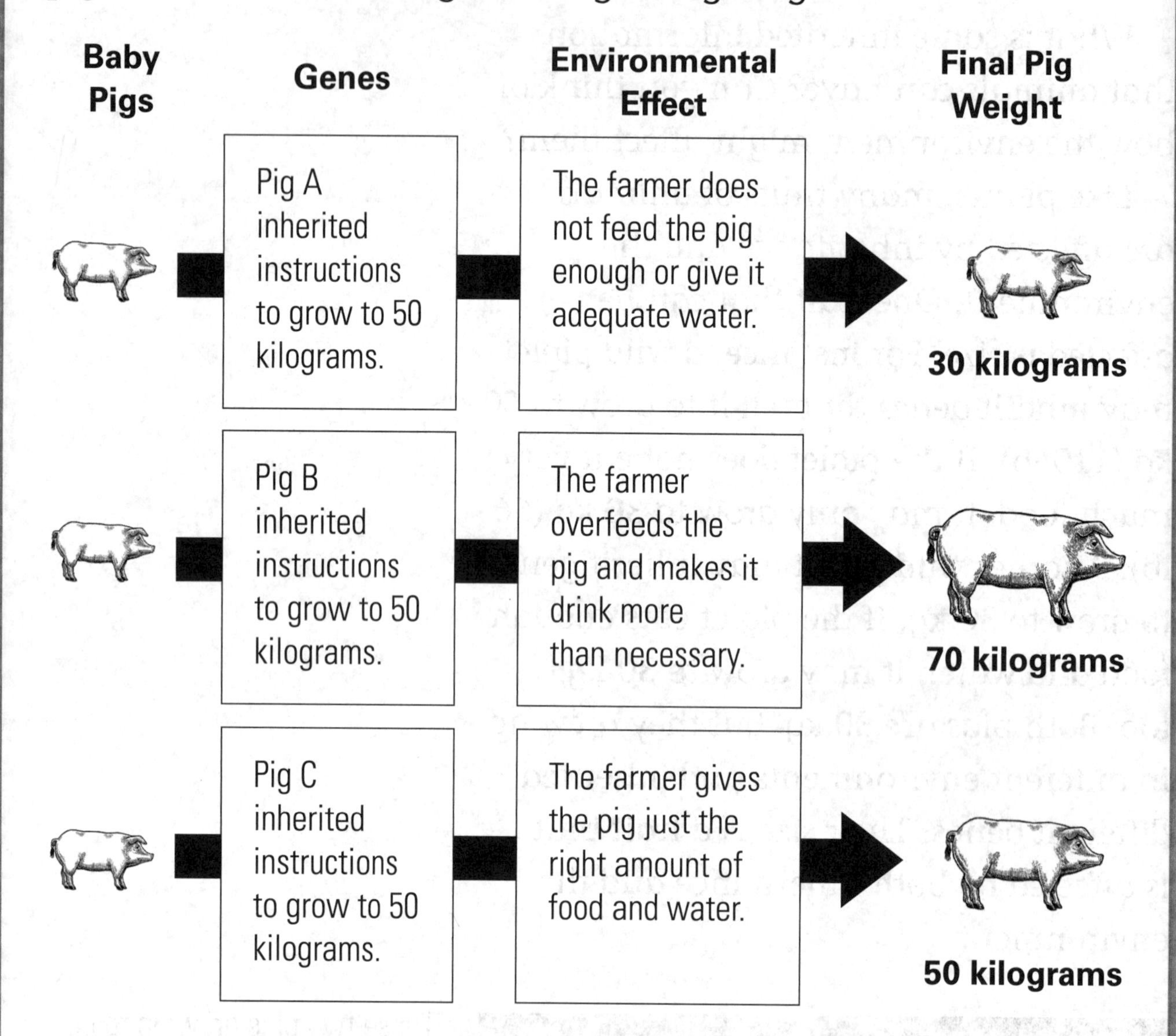

Which pig grew to the size it was expected to? Explain what happened to pigs A, B, and C. Use the following terms in your answer: **genes**, **environment**, and **combination**.

Show What You Know

Look at these two tree frogs. Read the paragraph.

Tree frogs spend most of their lives in trees. From their parents, they inherit well-developed suction cups at their finger and toe tips. They use these suction cups to hold onto leaves and even the smallest twigs in a tree. As some species of tree frogs move from a tree's branches to its leaves, an amazing change occurs! When they are on a branch, they are brown. When they move to a leaf, they can change to green. This helps them blend into their environment and stay safe from larger animals that like to eat them.

Offspring A = green

Offspring B = brown

Create a flowchart that explains how tree frog traits are both inherited from parents and affected by the environment.

Making Sense of the Phenomenon

Let's revisit the phenomenon: *By wintertime, some trees have lost all their leaves while some stay green all year.*

Think about:

- How are the trees' traits affected by the snow?
- Were these traits inherited?

Use your findings from the investigation to answer this question: *How will the tree's appearance change when the environment becomes warmer?*

Claim	
Evidence	
Reasoning	

☑ Go back to page 4 and fill out the unit checkpoint for this lesson.

NOTES

Lesson 4

Why Do Some Members of a Species Survive and Not Others?

Observing Phenomena

Discuss: Many animals have fur that is a similar color to the environment that they live in. Can you think of any examples?

Observe this phenomenon: *Most squirrels match their surroundings. It is very rare to find a pure white squirrel.*

Find It!

Are there squirrels near you? Do most of the squirrels match their surroundings?

Think of what you already know about why animals blend in with their environment. Write questions you have.

Modeling Birds Hunting for Moths

Start at one of the three stations around the classroom. There will be two groups at each.

- Each group will choose one student to play the role of a "bird" hunting for moths. These two students will cover their eyes.
- Birds, close your eyes. Everyone else will spread both groups' moths across the paper.
- When you hear "GO!", start hunting! You have 10 seconds. Pick the first moth you see and put it in the bin. Keep doing this until you hear "STOP!"
- Count how many of each moth you caught and record it. It's time for the next bird to hunt!

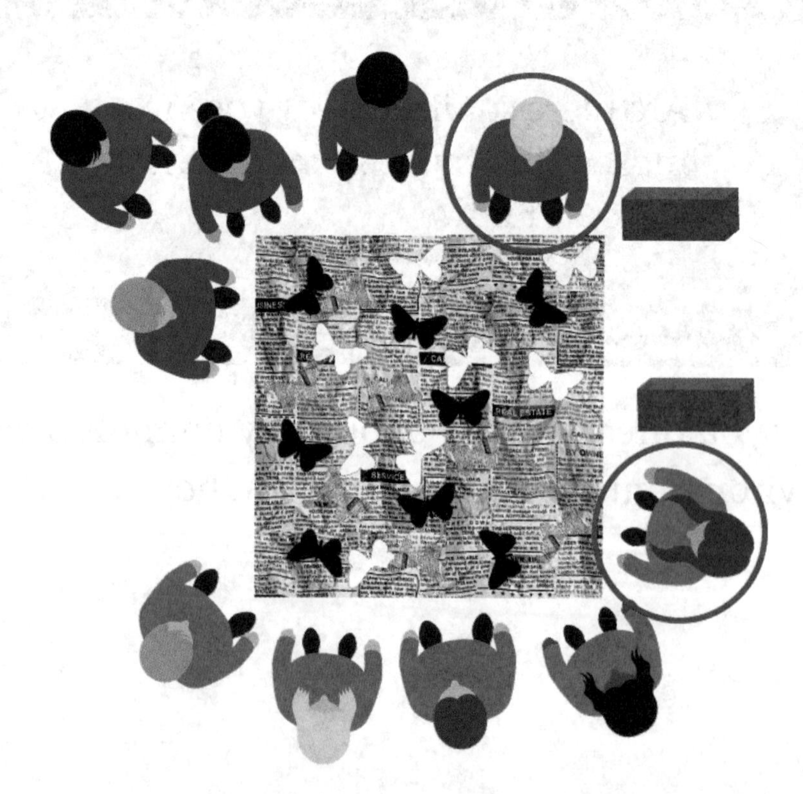

Write each group member's initials in the top row of the table. If you have less than five people in your group, some students will go twice.

Record the number of each moth color that each student in your group collects at each station.

Students collecting moths:							Total
Black Background	Black moths collected						
	White moths collected						
	Newspaper moths collected						
White Background	Black moths collected						
	White moths collected						
	Newspaper moths collected						
Newspaper Background	Black moths collected						
	White moths collected						
	Newspaper moths collected						

Interpreting Data

At each station, which type of moth was most likely to be caught? Which type was least likely to be caught?

Black Background:

White Background:

Newspaper Background:

Use patterns from your data to explain which type of moth is most likely to survive in each environment.

Vocabulary

Match the term to the correct definition.

Word Bank

survive   reproduce   camouflage   mate

________________ 1. When an animal's color makes it hard to see against a similarly colored background.

________________ 2. To stay alive.

________________ 3. An animal that can reproduce with another animal of the same species.

________________ 4. To make more of the same species of organism.

My Science Concepts

Reflect on your understanding. Draw an X along each line.

Camouflage is one trait that helps animals survive. Different members of the same species often have different camouflage patterns. These different patterns help some members of a species survive better than other members.

•————•————•————•————•

still learning **know it**

If all three stations (environments) were black, the black moths would have a better chance of surviving than the other two moths.

•————•————•————•————•

still learning **know it**

Scientists conduct many trials (rounds) of an experiment to find evidence for a pattern. Conducting only one or two rounds can lead to an incorrect explanation.

•————•————•————•————•

still learning **know it**

1. Survival Is Important to Organisms

What if dogs stopped making more dogs? There would be no more puppies on Earth. What would happen to dogs? They would soon disappear.

Organisms **reproduce**, or make more of their own species of organism. Producing offspring makes sure that there will be more members of a species. All living things reproduce.

Being able to *survive* is also important for all organisms. To **survive** means to stay alive. Some animals hunt other animals to survive. Those other animals try to avoid being eaten. For an eagle to survive, it must hunt and eat rabbits. For a rabbit to survive, it must run and hide from eagles.

Plants also try to survive. Plants need light to make food. A plant's leaves grow and move to take in more sunlight.

This jackrabbit needed to run away from the eagle to survive. If it were faster, it might have been able to avoid the eagle.

All organisms need to do two things. What two things are they, and why? To support your answer, quote from at least two parts of the text.

2. Some Individuals Do Not Survive or Reproduce

Lions live together in groups called prides. Members of the pride work together to hunt and catch prey. They all eat the food. By working together to hunt large prey, individual lions can get more food than they would on their own.

All animals try to survive and reproduce, but some individuals in a group fail. All lions in a pride need to eat to survive. But a small or weak lion may not be strong enough to fight with the other lions for food. An ill or injured lion may not be able to survive long enough to reproduce.

Some tomato plants in a garden will grow fruit. Other tomato plants may not. Insects or other animals may eat the leaves. The plant could become weak and die. It might not be able to grow seeds to make new plants.

This tomato plant may not reproduce, or it may produce fewer offspring. Its fruits are being eaten by insects.

Explain why some wolves may not get enough to eat. Use these terms in your answer: **survive, small**, and **injured**.

3. An Animal Has Traits That Help It Survive

Think about an octopus. What traits do you think it might have to help it survive?

Some individual animals have different traits that help them survive. For example, most species of octopus use *camouflage*. **Camouflage** is when an animal's color makes it hard to see. An octopus with good camouflage might be able to hide from sharks that want to eat it. Then it will survive. An octopus with worse camouflage may get eaten.

The length of a giraffe's neck is another trait that is different among individuals. Giraffes eat leaves from shrubs and trees. If a brush fire killed shrubs close to the ground, the giraffes would have only the tree leaves for food. Giraffes with longer necks may get more food than other giraffes. Those with shorter necks will not be able to reach as much food and they may not survive.

The neck length of a giraffe is a trait that varies among individuals. Giraffes with longer necks are able to reach more food than giraffes with shorter necks.

Draw a picture of a new animal species using your imagination. 
Label and describe the traits that will help the animal survive.

4. An Animal Has Traits That Help It Reproduce

Think about a group of lion cubs. The cubs' parents reproduced to make those offspring. But not all adult lions reproduce.

To reproduce, most animals must find a *mate*. A **mate** is another animal of the same species with which the animal can reproduce. One adult lion cannot reproduce. It needs to find another lion that can be its mate. But how do animals find mates?

Different individual animals find mates because of different traits they have. Males of some species have traits to help attract a mate. Male peacocks have large, colorful tail feathers. To attract a mate, male peacocks will raise their feathers and move them around. This is a trait that helps male peacocks find mates. If one male does not have these traits, he may not be able to reproduce.

This is a male peacock. He uses his large, bright feathers to attract mates so he can reproduce.

This is a male ostrich doing a very unique dance. Explain why you think the ostrich is dancing. Use these words in your answer: **mate, trait, reproduce**, and **attract**.

5. A Plant Has Traits That Help It Survive

An animal can run away or hide from enemies. Plants cannot run away from danger, but they have other traits that help them survive.

Some individual plants survive because they have different traits. Some plants have traits that keep animals from eating them. Many species of roses have stems with hard, sharp points called prickles. Prickles are painful to some animals, so they stay away. Rose plants with larger prickles will likely keep more animals away. A rose plant with a trait of fewer, smaller, or softer prickles may get eaten.

Some plants have traits that help them fight diseases. Elm trees can get a disease that kills them. Some elm trees have a trait that helps them fight off the disease and survive. Some do not have that trait and the disease kills them.

This rose plant has the trait of prickles. Prickles keep some animals from eating the rose, making it more likely to survive.

Explain why some plants survive and others do not. To answer this question, identify the main idea in the text. Find two specific examples to support your answer.

6. A Plant Has Traits That Help It Reproduce

Have you ever looked closely at a strawberry? Strawberries are covered with seeds. Even though all strawberries are covered with seeds, not all strawberry plants will reproduce.

To reproduce, a strawberry plant needs at least one of its seeds to grow into a new plant. For this to happen, a seed has to move away from its parent plant. One way this could happen is if a bird eats a strawberry and moves its seeds to new soil.

Some strawberry plants have different traits from other strawberry plants. Some have bigger berries. Some have sweeter berries. Strawberry plants with brighter or sweeter berries attract more birds. The seeds on these berries are more likely to grow into new plants. So, some plants of a species have traits that help them reproduce more than others.

This strawberry plant has big, sweet, red fruit. Having these large berries is a trait that will help this plant reproduce, because the fruits will attract more animals.

Draw a picture of a new plant species using your imagination. Label traits that will help the plant reproduce.

Show What You Know

Some members of a species have traits that give them advantages over other individuals. Look at each image and read the description next to it. Then, in your own words, explain how differences in a trait help that organism.

Many birds sing to attract mates. They usually go to a high perch where their song will carry further. Some birds in a species can sing more loudly than others. Their voice travels farther and reaches more birds of their species.

Some watermelon plants produce small fruits or ones that are less sweet. People like plants that make large, sweet melons, like this one. So they plant more of these plants' seeds.

Making Sense of the Phenomenon

Let's revisit the phenomenon: *Most squirrels match their surroundings. It is very rare to find a pure white squirrel.*

Think about:

- Does a white squirrel match its surroundings?
- Does a squirrel's trait of white fur make it more or less likely to survive?

Use your findings from the investigation to answer this question: *Why is it rare to find a white squirrel?*

Claim	
Evidence	
Reasoning	

☑ Go back to page 4 and fill out the unit checkpoint for this lesson.

Performance Assessment: Writing for Science Monthly

You're on assignment! Science Monthly is sending you to Ecuador to investigate organisms and their traits.

You will:

- analyze pictures of plant and animal families and find patterns within the families.
- read and write about a frog that loses its toxicity when removed from the rainforest.
- read and write about trait variations of different Ecuadorian plants and animals.

Touring Ecuador

Let's tour Ecuador! You'll visit three locations.

At each location, you'll learn about a species that lives there. You'll use this information to write an article.

Get a copy of *Handout C: Tour Stops*. As you read about the organism at each stop, complete the chart below.

Organism	Trait for survival or reproduction	How this trait helps the organism	How this trait can vary
Harmless frog species	Yellow stripes on shoulders and legs		Some frogs don't have yellow stripes.
Male frigatebirds			
Galápagos prickly pears			

What are the similarities between the organisms you read about?

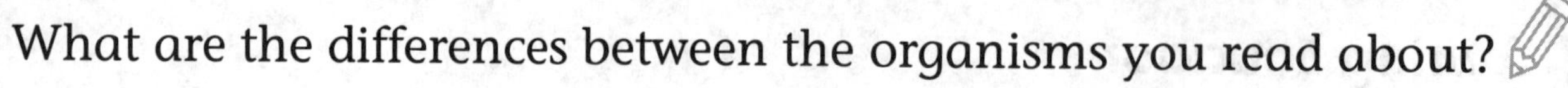

What are the differences between the organisms you read about?

Complete the cause-and-effect chart below.

Organism	Cause (trait)	Effect
Harmless frog species	Yellow stripes	
Male frigatebirds	Larger gular sac	
Galápagos prickly pears		Less likely to survive because tortoises eat their paddles

Writing an Article About Trait Differences

Review the notes you made about the harmless frog species, male frigatebirds, and Galápagos prickly pears.

Write an article that answers this question: *How do differences in a trait help an individual survive and reproduce?*

- Give the article an appropriate title.
- Start with a claim that answers the question above.
- Use evidence from the organisms you learned about on the tour of Ecuador to support the claim.
- Explain how the evidence supports the claim.

Lesson 5

What Are the Life Cycles of Plants?

Observing Phenomena

Discuss: Have you ever had a fruit that has a seed on the inside?

Observe this phenomenon: *Some plants, like this tomato plant, form fruits with seeds inside.*

Try It! Start a garden yourself! With the help of an adult, plant some seeds in the ground. After a few weeks, what do you observe about the seeds?

Think of what you already know about fruits that have seeds in the middle. Write questions you have.

Modeling Each Stage of a Life Cycle

In this investigation, you will model the four stages of a sunflower's life cycle—birth, growth, reproduction, and death.

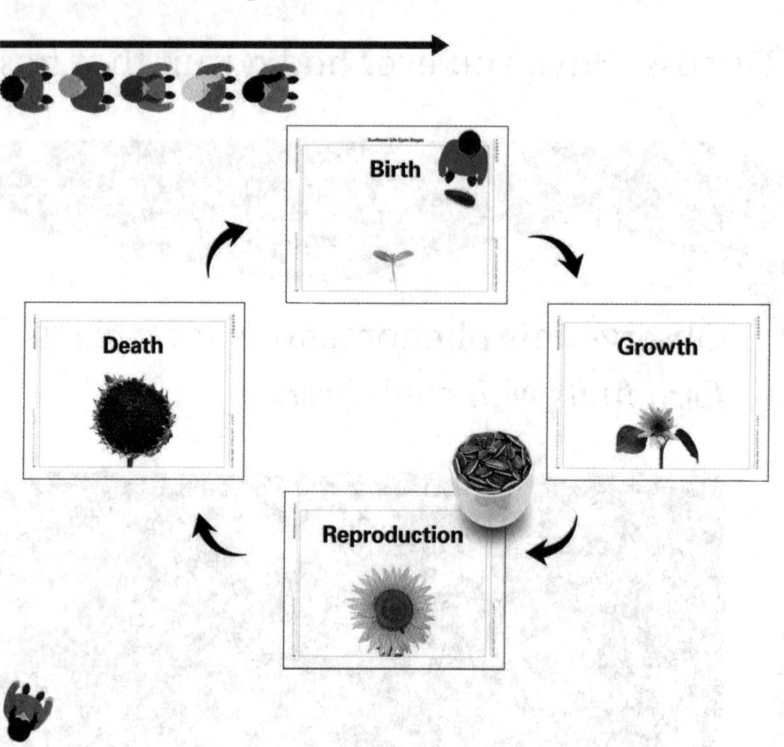

As you watch the following videos and take notes. Write or draw any ideas you have.

Debriefing the Experience

Write in the name of each stage of a sunflower's life cycle. Then, draw a picture showing what happens during each stage.

Life Cycle of the Common Sunflower

a) ______________________ b) ______________________

d) ______________________ c) ______________________

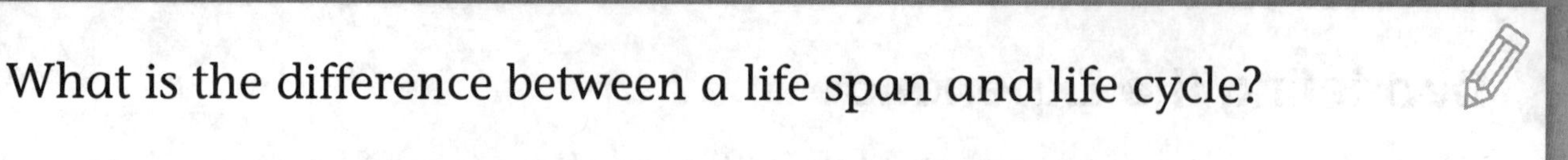

What is the difference between a life span and life cycle?

Read each statement about a part of the life cycle below. Then, number them from 1 to 4. "1" is the thing that would happen first, and "4" is the thing that would happen last.

________ a) After a common sunflower makes new seeds, it dies. Its offspring repeat the pattern of life.

________ b) Over time, the seedling can grow into an adult plant with flowers.

________ c) Each sunflower begins its life as a seed. With the right conditions, it sprouts into a seedling.

________ d) If the wind or an insect transfers pollen to the flower, a seed can develop.

Vocabulary

Write in the term that matches the definition.

Word Bank

life span | fruit | flower | life cycle | seed

____________________ 1. The pattern of changes that a member of a species goes through during its lifetime.

____________________ 2. The typical amount of time that most members of a species live, from birth to death.

____________________ 3. The part of a plant that surrounds and protects the seeds.

____________________ 4. A part of some plants where seeds are made.

____________________ 5. A small, protected part of a plant that can grow into an adult offspring.

My Science Concepts

Reflect on your understanding. Draw an X along each line.

A life span is how long an organism typically lives. Some plants live for longer than others.

still learning **know it**

Many adult plants produce seeds. Seeds have a tiny plant inside that can sprout and grow into an adult plant. Many seeds have fruit that surrounds and protects them.

still learning **know it**

A life cycle describes the pattern of change that a species goes through in its life. You can make predictions based on these patterns.

still learning **know it**

1. Plants Have Different Life Spans

Suppose you are walking through the woods. You see some plants that are alive. They have green leaves and bright flowers. You also see plants that are dead, like a tree that has fallen down.

A **life span** is the typical amount of time that members of a species live, from birth to death. Different species have different life spans. During an organism's life span, it grows, develops, and tries to reproduce. For example, common sunflowers live for less than one year. Their life span is one growing season. Some other plant species have longer life spans. Apple trees, for example, have life spans of 100 years. Some trees have even longer life spans. Redwood trees can live for over 1,000 years!

These common sunflowers have a life span of only one growing season. These adult plants will all die before the end of the year.

In your own words, explain what the life span of a plant is. Do all plants have the same life span?

2. Plants Reproduce

Think of the different flowers you have seen. Many plants produce flowers. What do flowers do for the plant?

A **flower** is the part in some plants where *seeds* are made. A **seed** is a small, protected part of a plant that can grow into an adult offspring. All plants need to reproduce. Plants that grow flowers do this by producing seeds. To grow seeds, flowers need *pollen*. Pollen is also grown in flowers, but it usually moves from one flower to another. Wind and insects can move pollen. Pollen sticks to insects when they land on flowers. The insect may fly to another flower of the same species. Some of its pollen will rub off there.

Each of these seeds is able to grow into a new plant. The fruits and their seeds all grew from flowers.

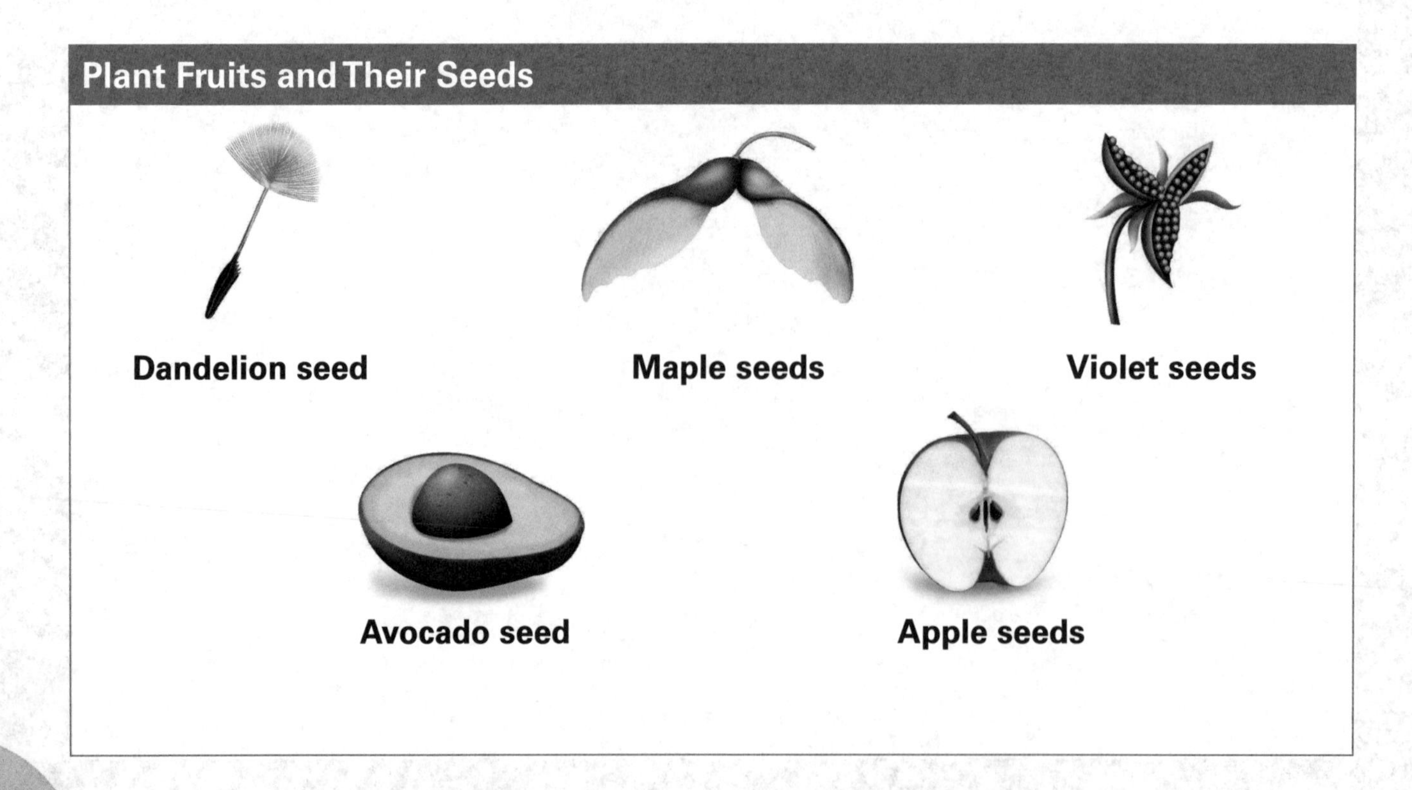

After pollen gets to the flower, a *fruit* develops and seeds form inside of it. A **fruit** is the part of a plant that surrounds and protects a seed. Some flowering plants have juicy fruits, like an apple. Others have dry fruits, like dandelions.

Explain what is happening in this image. Use the following terms in your answer: **bee, flower, pollen, seed,** and **fruit**. 

3. Sunflowers Have a Life Cycle

When scientists observe how living things grow, they look for patterns. A *pattern* is something, such as a series of changes, that repeats.

Plants go through a series of changes as they grow. The pattern of changes that a member of a species goes through during its lifetime is called a **life cycle**.

Common sunflower plants go through different stages in their life cycle. Each sunflower begins its life as a seed. If the seed has enough water and is warm enough, it sprouts into a seedling. Over time, the seedling can grow into an adult plant. Adult sunflower plants can make flowers. With enough sunshine and water, the flowers can make new seeds. Each sunflower seed is surrounded by a tiny, dry fruit that protects the seed inside. Finally, after a common sunflower makes new seeds, it dies. A sunflower's life cycle is a pattern that its offspring repeat.

A common sunflower plant goes through its full life cycle in less than a year. At the end of the growing season, it dies and drops seeds that begin the life cycle again.

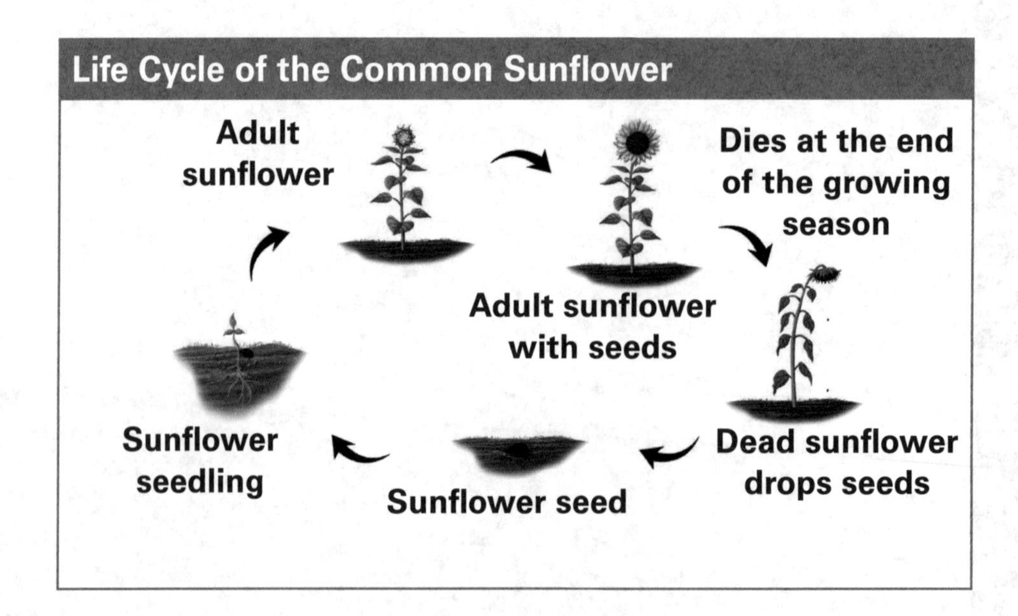

In each circle, draw a picture of a sunflower in the correct stage of its life cycle. You should draw a seed, a seedling, a fully grown plant with a flower, a plant that has developed new seeds, and a plant that has reached the end of its life span and died.

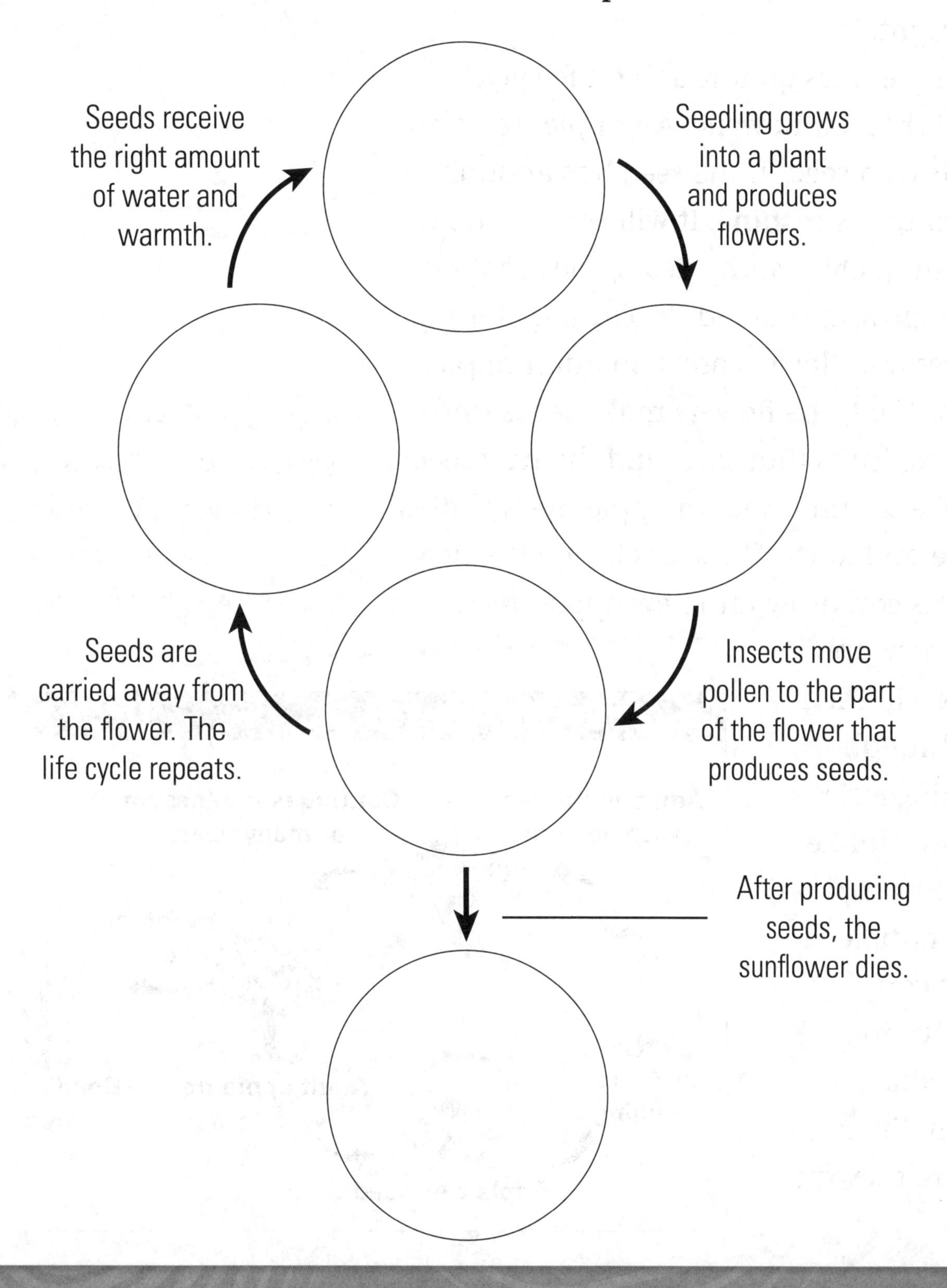

4. Apple Trees Have a Life Cycle

When you last ate an apple, did you see the seeds inside? Those tiny seeds can grow into big apple trees if the conditions are right.

Apple trees go through a life cycle similar to sunflowers'. An apple tree also starts as a seed. If the seed has enough water and sunshine, it will sprout into a seedling. Over many years, the seedling may grow into an adult plant. In spring, leaves and flowers grow on adult apple trees. Next, the flowers make seeds and apples, fruits that surround the new seeds. Unlike a sunflower, an apple tree's fruit is large and juicy. The seeds inside the new apples can grow into new apple trees. The new apple trees will then go through the life cycle again. Unlike sunflowers, adult apple trees can survive to reproduce many times before they die.

An apple tree makes fruits with seeds, but not until it has grown for several years. The adult apple tree can survive for many years and make new fruit each year.

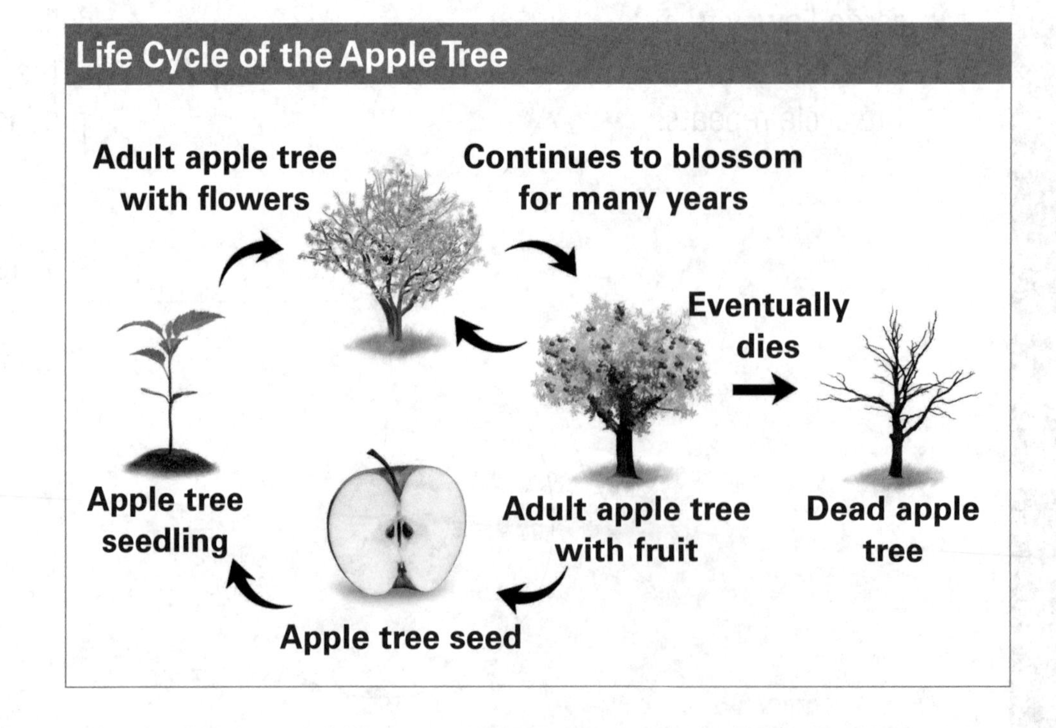

Look at the diagram of an apple tree's life cycle below. In each box, write in your own words how the apple tree is changing during that stage of its life cycle.

Show What You Know

Write a story about the life of a sunflower seed. Your story must:

- identify and explain four typical stages in the life cycle of a sunflower.
- use sequence language, such as "first," "next," and "finally."
- include the following terms: **birth**, **growth**, **reproduction**, **death**, **pattern**, and **life cycle**.

Making Sense of the Phenomenon

Let's revisit the phenomenon: *Some plants, like this tomato plant, form fruits with seeds inside.*

Think about:

- Why do plants produce flowers, seeds, or fruits?

Use your findings from the investigation to answer this question: *How does a tomato plant reproduce?*

Claim	
Evidence	
Reasoning	

☑ Go back to page 4 and fill out the unit checkpoint for this lesson.

Lesson 6

What Are the Life Cycles of Animals with Backbones?

Observing Phenomena

Discuss: What animals can you think of that hatch from eggs?

Observe this phenomenon: *Animals like ducks or birds hatch from eggs.*

See It! Look around the trees outside. Do you see any bird nests with eggs inside? What will happen to the birds developing inside those eggs?

Think of what you already know about types of animals that hatch from eggs. Write questions you have.

Assigning Animals

Now we are going to learn about the life cycles of many different vertebrates!

Each group will be assigned to one of these animal species. Circle your assigned animal.

You will learn about your species' life cycle. Then, you will write, record, and present a story about its life cycle.

Learning About Your Animal's Life Cycle

Read the life cycle descriptions on *Handout A: Vertebrate Life Cycle Descriptions*. Put the four statements in order from birth to death. Then, glue them below.

Birth

Growth

Reproduction

Death

Creating Your Story

Using the information on your handout, plan your presentation below.

- Write a story that explains all four stages of your animal's life cycle. Be creative and tell the story in a fun way!
- Choose the images that you will project for the class as they listen to each stage. Write the letter of the image from your handout that your group feels best shows each stage. Pick images that best match your story.

Script	Image
Birth:	
Growth:	
Reproduction:	
Death:	

Vocabulary

Which statement describes a **vertebrate**? Which describes **metamorphosis**?

______________________ 1. An animal with a backbone.

______________________ 2. A large change in body shape during the life cycle of some animal species.

My Science Concepts

Reflect on your understanding. Draw an X along each line.

Animals with backbones are grouped together as vertebrates. Vertebrates include mammals, birds, fish, reptiles, and amphibians.

still learning — **know it**

Most baby mammals grow and develop inside their mother's body. The mother then gives birth. Offspring are born, then grow into adults.

still learning — **know it**

Birds lay eggs and so do many kinds of reptiles and fish. Offspring hatch from the eggs, grow, reproduce, and eventually die.

still learning — **know it**

An amphibian's life cycle would include metamorphosis, or a large change in body shape, like a tadpole developing legs as it becomes an adult frog.

still learning — **know it**

1. Some Animals Have Backbones

Think of animals you know about. Some may have fur. Others have feathers or scales. If you have ever touched the back of an animal with fur, feathers, or scales, you may have felt a line of bones under its skin. This is its backbone.

Animals can be grouped by whether or not they have backbones. Animals that have backbones are called **vertebrates**. Vertebrates are classified into seven smaller animal groups. Mammals, reptiles, and birds are vertebrates. So are fish and amphibians. Cats, elephants, and humans are mammals. Snakes, lizards, and turtles are reptiles. Parrots and ducks are birds. Goldfish and sharks are fish. Frogs and salamanders are amphibians.

Cats are vertebrates. If you pet a cat, you can feel its backbone.

Write the letters of the two animals in these images that are vertebrates. Then, in your own words, explain why each is a vertebrate.

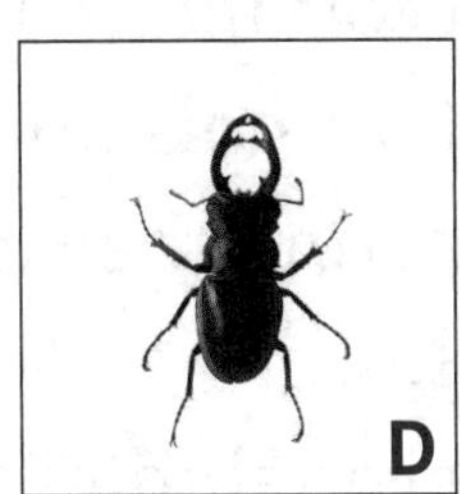

Vertebrate ________

Vertebrate ________

2. Mammals Have a Similar Life Cycle

What do cats, dogs, elephants, and humans have in common? They are all mammals! Mammals have some traits in common, and they also have similar life cycles.

Mammals are vertebrates that can produce milk for their young. They are also covered in hair. Mammals keep their bodies at a steady temperature. Their body temperature stays the same, even when the temperature of their environment changes. That means that a bear keeps itself cool in the summer and warm in the winter.

Most mammals live on land. But some mammals live in water. Whales spend their entire lives in water. They come up to the water's surface to breathe air. Some mammals, like river otters, live both on land and in water.

Most baby mammals grow and develop inside of their mother's body. Each mammal species develops in its own amount of time. Baby mice develop in about three weeks. It takes more than a year and a half for baby elephants to develop.

Bats are mammals that can fly. Like other mammals, they feed their young with milk. Elephants are very large mammals. They live on land and are covered with small hairs.

After baby mammals have developed, the mother gives birth. Their parents take care of them while they are young. When young mammals grow into adults, they can reproduce. The cycle begins again. Many mammals can reproduce several times during their lives.

Different mammals have different life spans. Harp seals can live for 35 years. Most mice only live for about two years. But the shortest mammal life span is under one year for some mouse species. Bowhead whales can live for almost 200 years!

Mice develop inside their mother's body until they are born. Their mothers take care of them when they are babies, until they grow into adults.

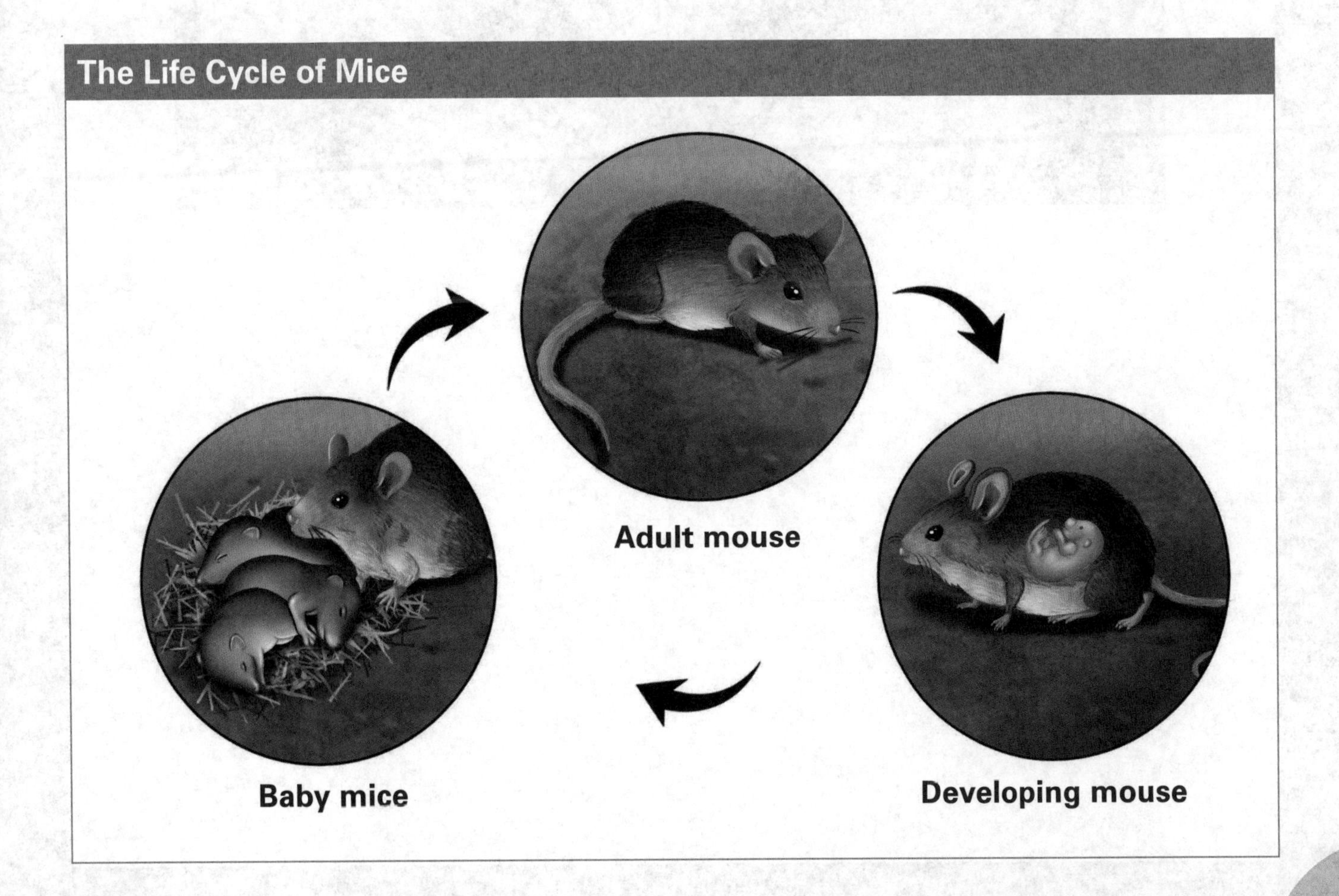

Gorillas are mammals. Describe a gorilla's life cycle using the following terms: **reproduce, young, develop, care, adult,** and **born**.

3. Bird, Reptile, and Fish Life Cycles Are Similar

Can you think of something that birds, reptiles, and fish have in common? They are all vertebrates, and they all lay eggs! Their life cycles are similar, but not exactly the same.

All bird life cycles begin with an egg. A baby bird grows and develops inside of the egg, which has a hard shell. Most of the time, adult birds keep the eggs warm and protect them while the baby birds develop.

When baby birds are grown and developed enough, the eggs hatch. Most parents feed and protect the babies until they can leave the nest, and even afterwards. When the baby birds grow into adults, they can lay their own eggs, starting the life cycle over again.

Different birds can also have different life spans. Mourning doves only live for about a year and a half, while many parrots can live to be over 50!

This is a young robin. Like many young birds, it cannot fly or feed itself. So, its parents take care of it.

Most reptiles have a life cycle that also starts with an egg. The shell develops around the egg inside of the mother's body. The young reptiles that hatch look like small adults. Some young snakes grow into adult snakes in about a year. Adult snakes can then lay new eggs, repeating their life cycle.

Fish are also vertebrates that hatch from eggs. Fish life cycles take place in water. Some fish live in salty oceans. Others live in fresh water. Most fish eggs are laid in water but, unlike bird and reptile eggs, fish eggs do not have a shell. Adult fish that survive long enough can lay new eggs, starting their life cycle over again.

The changes that birds, reptiles, and fish go through during their lives form patterns. There are many similarities between their life cycles.

Unlike most baby birds, this baby turtle can take care of itself as soon as it hatches. It is able to crawl and swim.

What are **two** things that are similar between bird, reptile, and fish life cycles?

What is **one** thing that is different about a bird's life cycle?

What is **one** thing that is different about a reptile's life cycle?

What is **one** thing that is different about a fish's life cycle?

4. Amphibians Go Through Metamorphosis

Frogs, toads, and salamanders are amphibians. How does a baby amphibian differ from an adult?

Amphibians have life cycles that are different from other vertebrates. Amphibians go through *metamorphosis*. **Metamorphosis** is a large change in body shape that happens during the life cycles of some animal species.

Adult female frogs lay eggs without shells in water. Tadpoles hatch from the eggs. Tadpoles have a tail and breathe underwater. They do not look like their parents. The tadpoles grow larger and start to go through metamorphosis. Four legs grow, and the tail disappears. The tadpole develops into a small frog that breathes air and can live on land. Soon, the frog can reproduce and the life cycle repeats.

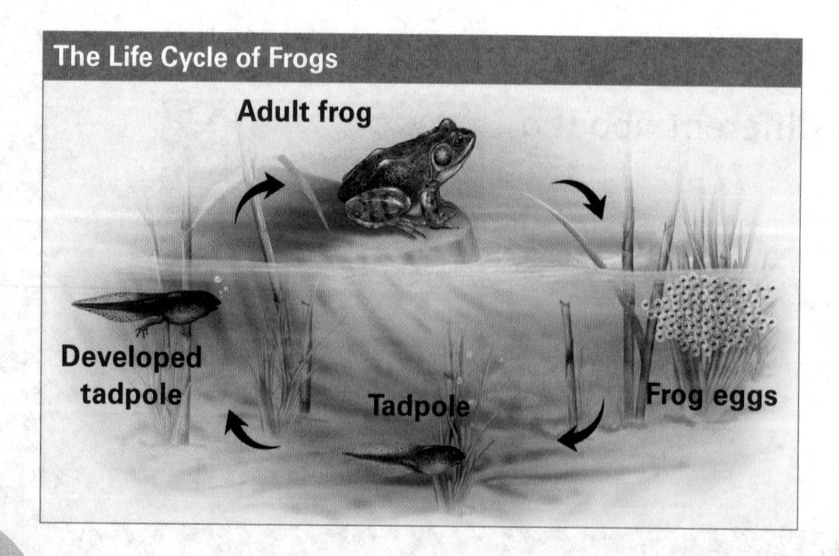

Frog eggs are laid underwater and eventually hatch into tadpoles. Tadpoles also live underwater but will go through metamorphosis and become an adult frog.

Complete the life cycle diagram below by writing the name of each stage and drawing a picture of it. Use the labels and photos below as hints. One has been filled in for you.

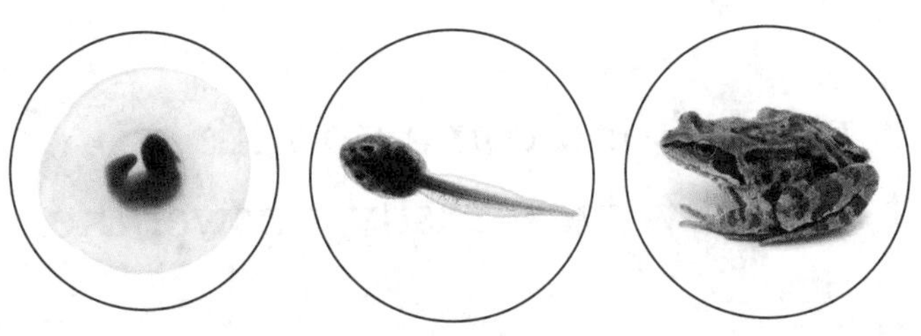

adult frog
tadpole
frog egg

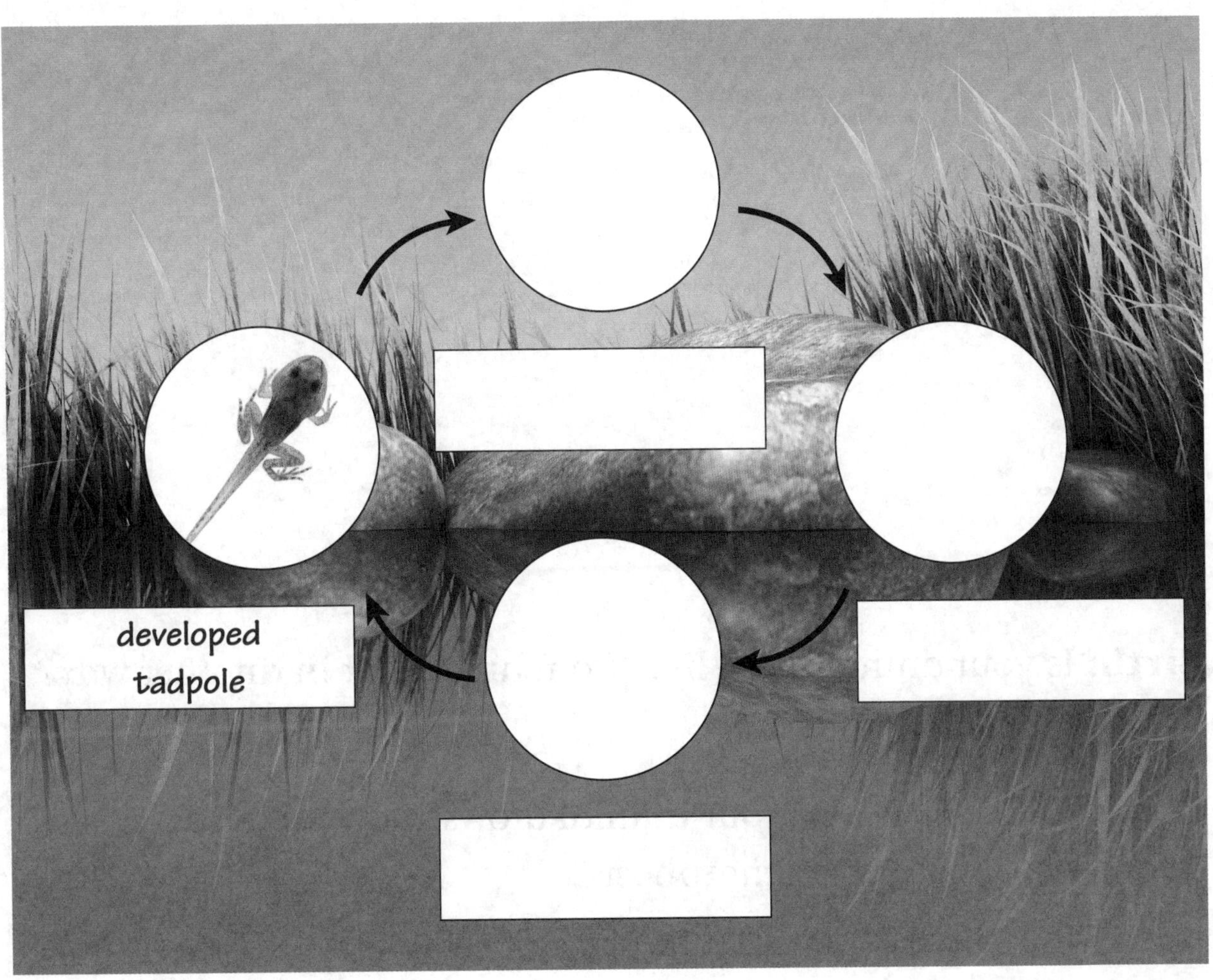

Show What You Know

You have learned that vertebrates have unique and varied life cycles. Now create your own vertebrate and predict its life cycle!

First, draw a picture of your new animal and come up with a name. Then, decide how long it typically lives. Lastly, answer the questions below.

Birth: Is your animal born live, from an egg, or in another way?

Growth: Describe how your animal grows. How large can it get? Does it go through metamorphosis?

Reproduction: How does your animal find a mate? How many offspring does it have?

Death: How long is the lifespan of your vertebrate?

Making Sense of the Phenomenon

Let's revisit the phenomenon: *Animals like ducks or birds hatch from eggs.*

Think about:

- What other kinds of animals have a life cycle similar to birds?
- Do mammals have similar life cycles to birds?

Use your findings from the investigation to answer this question: *Why don't humans hatch from eggs?*

Claim	
Evidence	
Reasoning	

☑ Go back to page 4 and fill out the unit checkpoint for this lesson.

Lesson 7
What Are the Life Cycles of Animals Without Backbones?

Observing Phenomena

Discuss: Think about the other types of animals around the world. Do you think their bone structures are the same?

Observe this phenomenon: *This cicada insect is leaving behind its old skin*

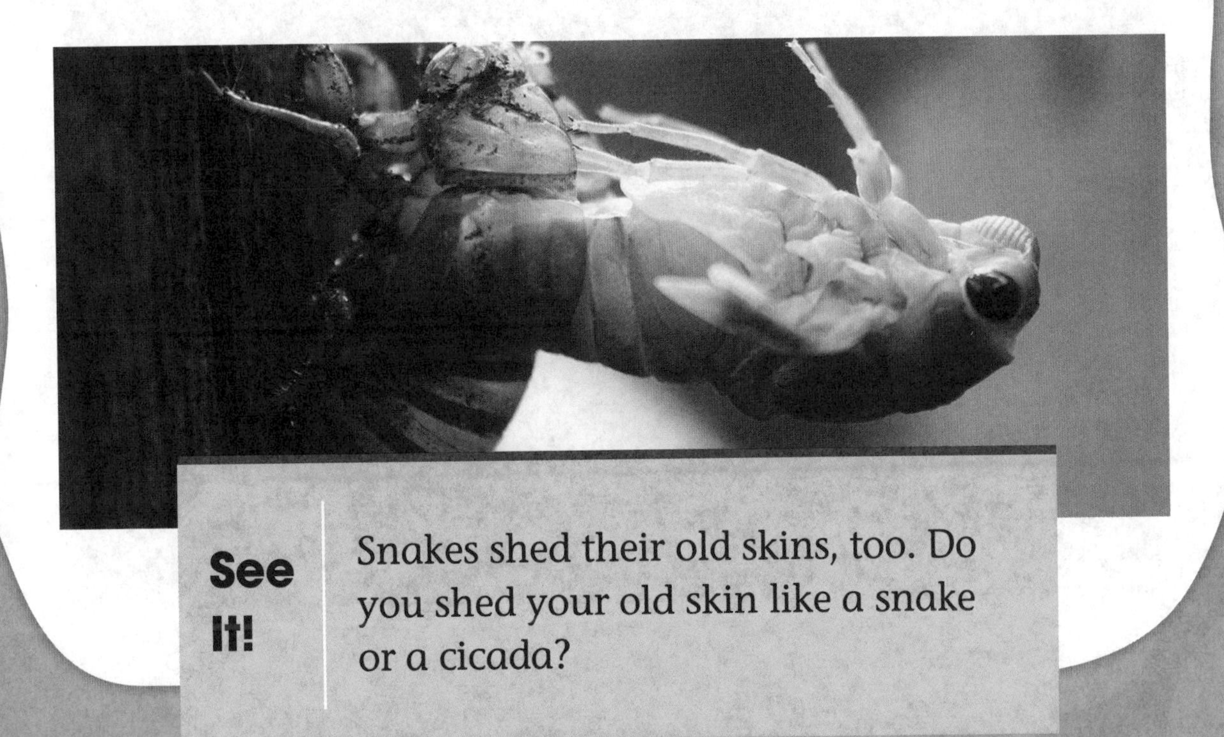

See It!

Snakes shed their old skins, too. Do you shed your old skin like a snake or a cicada?

Think of what you already know about the bone structures of different animals. Write questions you have.

Observing and Caring for Butterflies

In this investigation, you will observe the life cycle of a butterfly. You will compare this model to the life cycles of plants and animals with backbones.

Draw a picture of each stage of a butterfly's life cycle. Include the two parts of the growth stage in butterflies.

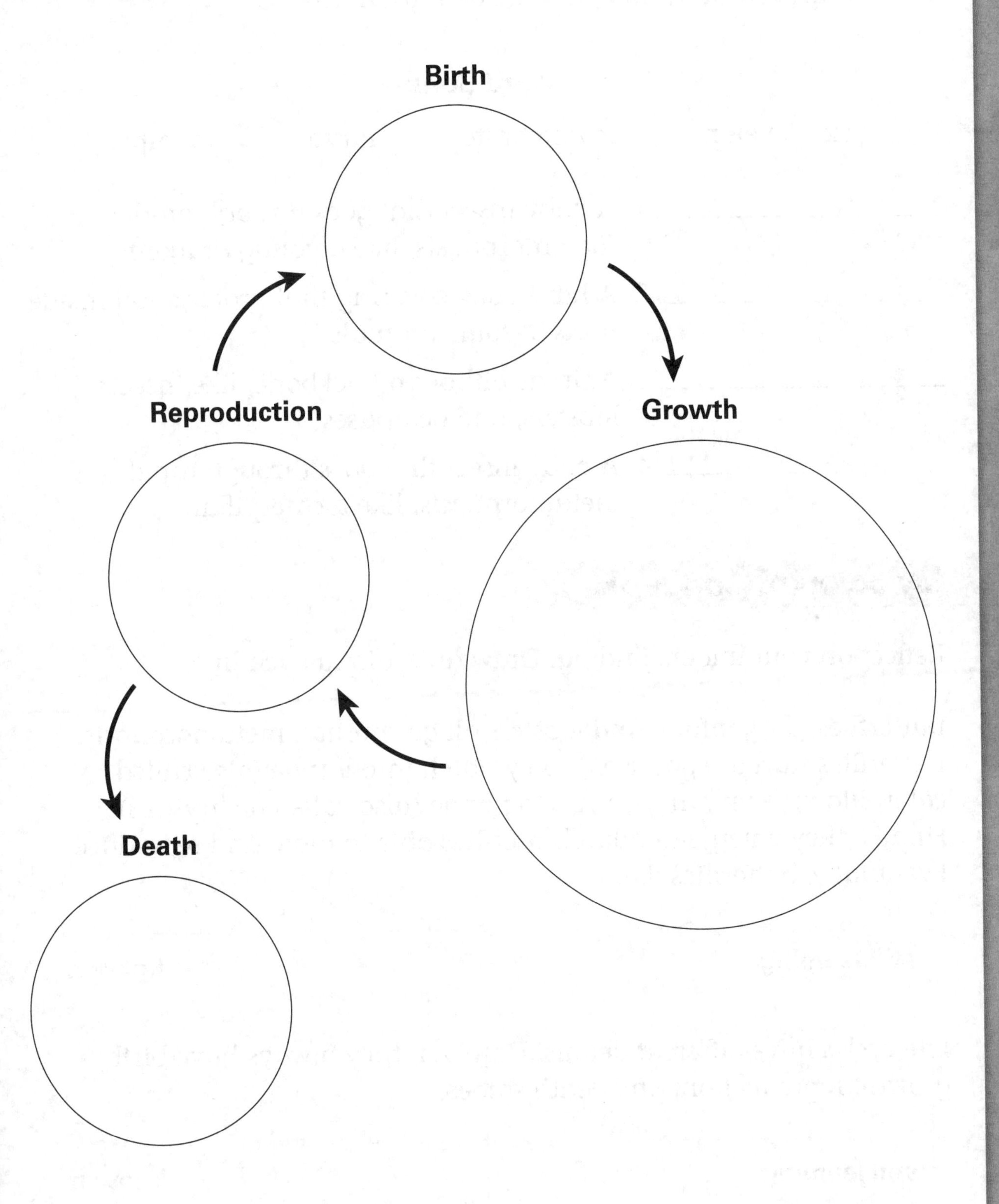

Vocabulary

Write in the term that matches the definition.

Word Bank

exoskeleton   invertebrate   larva   nymph

________________ 1. A baby insect that goes through gradual metamorphosis, like a young dragonfly.

________________ 2. A hard body covering that protects soft inside parts of some animals.

________________ 3. Animal without a backbone, like insects, lobsters, and octopuses.

________________ 4. A baby insect that goes through rapid metamorphosis, like a caterpillar.

My Science Concepts

Reflect on your understanding. Draw an X along each line.

Butterflies, dragonflies, and lobsters all go through metamorphosis. Butterflies start as eggs. Next, they hatch into larvae (also called caterpillars). Then, they turn into pupae (also called a chrysalis). Finally, they emerge as adult butterflies able to mate and reproduce. Eventually, butterflies die.

still learning ●———●———●———●———● **know it**

Life cycles have different details. However, they always have birth, growth, reproduction, and death stages.

still learning ●———●———●———●———● **know it**

1. Some Animals Do Not Have Backbones

What do spiders, honeybees, and crabs all have in common? They all do not have backbones.

Animals without backbones are called **invertebrates**. Most animal species on Earth are invertebrates. Many invertebrates, such as insects, have a hard body covering called an **exoskeleton** instead of bones. Exoskeletons protect the soft insides of most invertebrates. However, exoskeletons cannot grow. So, many invertebrates shed them and grow new ones as they grow larger.

Not all invertebrates have exoskeletons, though. For example, octopuses are invertebrates. They are able to move through spaces that are much smaller than their bodies. They can do this because they do not have a skeleton.

Invertebrates are animals without backbones. Insects have exoskeletons, like the one on the left, which was shed by a cicada. An octopus, shown on the right, has no skeleton at all.

Explain what these two insects have in common. Use these terms in your answer: **invertebrate, exoskeleton,** and **backbone**.

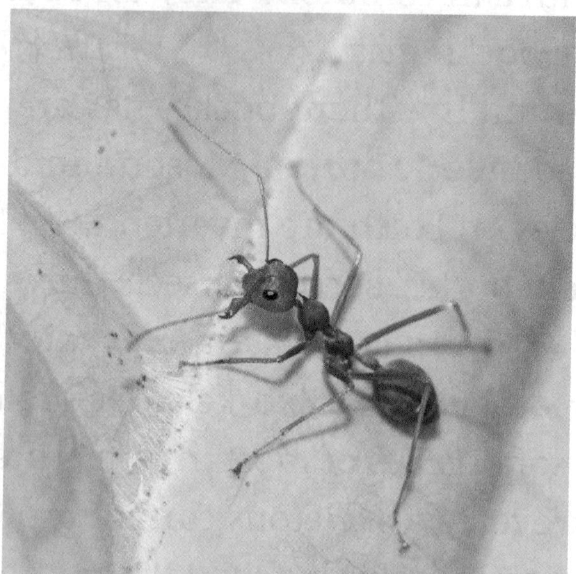

2. Butterflies Go Through Metamorphosis

You have probably seen butterflies near flowers. Some butterflies are brightly colored. Some have patterns on their wings.

You may have also seen a young butterfly. It does not look like an adult butterfly. It does not have wings or legs like the adult's. Like amphibians, most insects go through metamorphosis. They go through a large change in body shape during their life cycle. The changes many insects go through form a pattern.

The life cycle of butterflies has four stages. It starts with an egg. An adult female butterfly lays eggs with thin shells on a plant leaf.

A butterfly's life cycle has four stages. After it becomes an adult, the butterfly can lay eggs, and the life cycle will repeat.

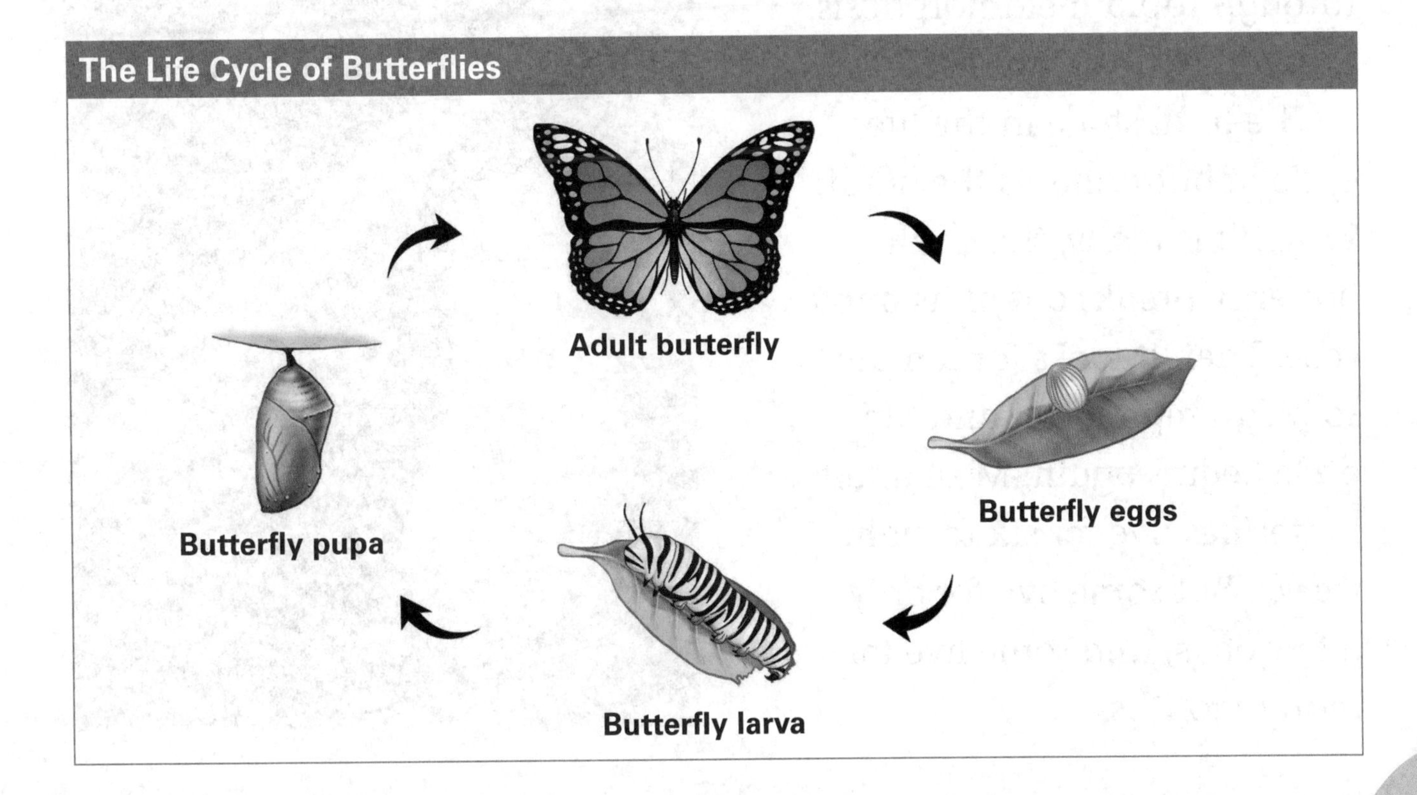

A wormlike creature hatches from the egg. This second stage in the the life cycle of many invertebrates is called a **larva.** A butterfly larva, also called a *caterpillar,* looks nothing like its parents.

A butterfly larva spends almost all its time eating and growing. It must grow a new exoskeleton many times because the old ones become too small.

The last time a larva sheds, its body shape changes. Now it is called a *pupa.* A pupa is the third stage in the life cycle of butterflies and some other insects. A pupa does not eat, and it stays in one place. Inside the pupa, an adult butterfly is taking shape. Wings and legs develop. The pupa goes through rapid metamorphosis. It becomes an adult insect.

The final stage in the life cycle of butterflies is the adult. When it is ready, the adult butterfly breaks out of its pupa case. Then it looks for a mate so it can reproduce, and the cycle begins again. Most adult butterflies live for six to eight weeks. But some live for only a few days, and some live for many months.

This is a new monarch butterfly pupa. The pupa will go through metamorphosis and become an adult.

Use this diagram to describe the butterfly life cycle. Include all these terms in your answer: **pupa, adult, caterpillar, metamorphosis, larva,** and **egg**.

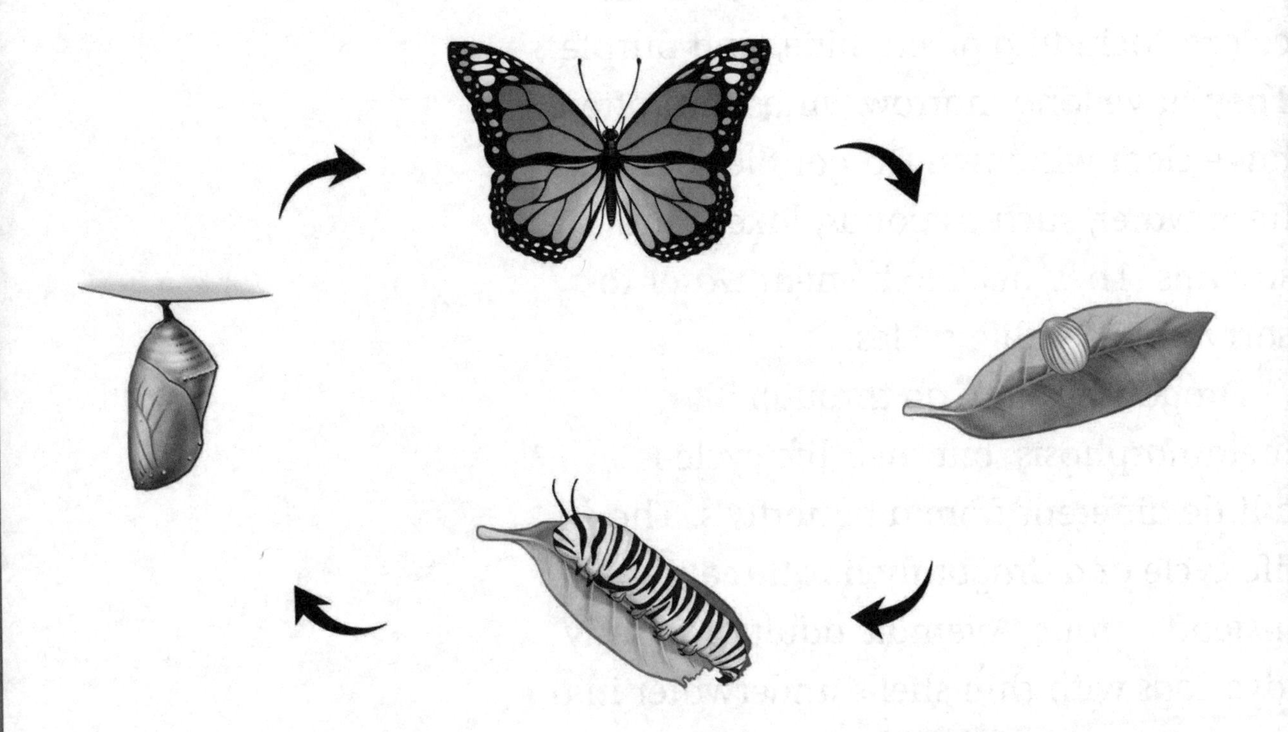

3. Dragonflies Go Through Metamorphosis

You may have seen dragonflies flying quickly through the air. Dragonflies are insects. Dragonfly bodies may be many colors, including green, blue, and purple. They have long, narrow wings that often have clear windows. Dragonflies live near fresh water, such as ponds, lakes, and streams. They need to be near water to carry out their life cycles.

Dragonflies also go through metamorphosis, but their life cycle is a little different from a butterfly's. The life cycle of a dragonfly has three stages instead of four. A female adult dragonfly lays eggs with thin shells underwater in a pond. She often lays them on the stems of underwater plants. The eggs are the first stage of the dragonfly's life cycle.

This is an adult dragonfly. Adult dragonflies live near fresh water so they can reproduce and find food.

In a few weeks, baby dragonflies called *nymphs* hatch out of the eggs. **Nymphs** are young insects that go through gradual metamorphosis. Nymphs are the second stage of a dragonfly's life cycle. They do not look exactly like adult dragonflies. Nymphs do not have wings and cannot fly. They live underwater while they grow and develop. Nymphs hunt and eat insects in water. As nymphs grow, they shed their exoskeleton and grow a new, larger one many times. Sometimes this stage takes many years.

Once a nymph is fully grown, it crawls up the stem of a plant and out of the water. It finishes its metamorphosis by shedding its skin to become an adult dragonfly. Adult dragonflies have wings and do not live underwater anymore. Many adult dragonflies have a life span of about two months. So, they must find mates quickly to reproduce.

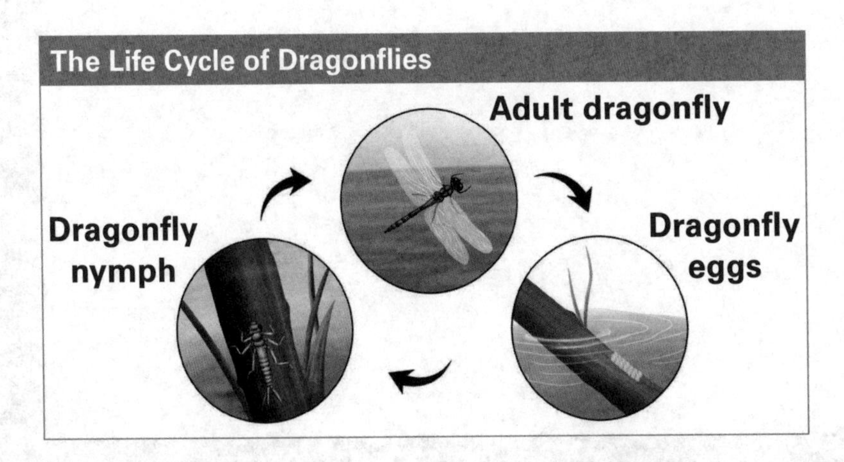

Female adult dragonflies lay eggs underwater. When a nymph hatches, it begins to grow and change. When the nymph changes into an adult, the metamorphosis is finished.

The diagram below shows a dragonfly's life cycle. Describe what happens in each of the stages in the diagram.

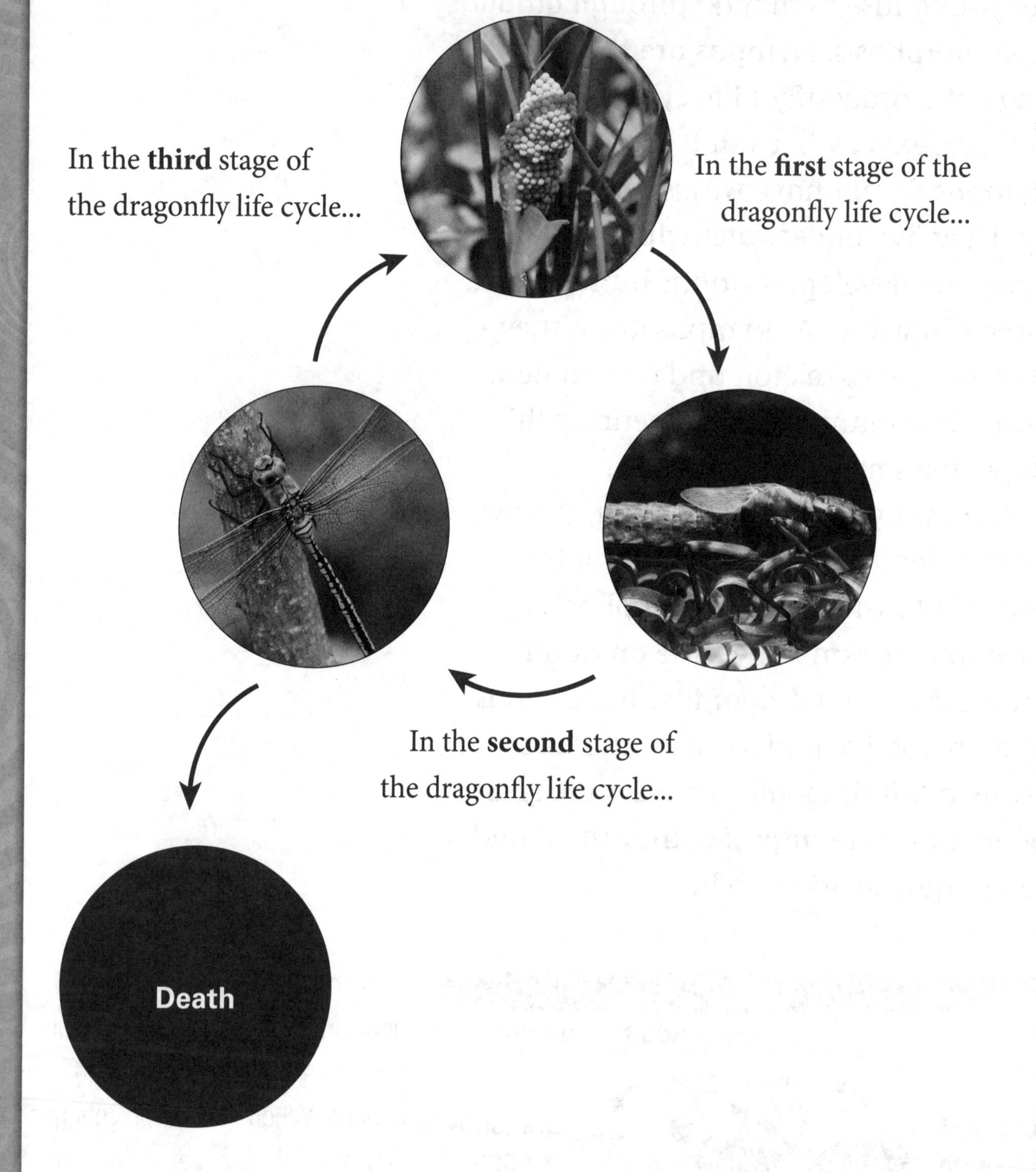

4. Lobster Life Cycles

Insects are not the only kinds of invertebrates. Crabs, crayfish, and lobsters are, too. How do these animals compare?

Crabs, crayfish, and lobsters have exoskeletons, just like insects. They also go through metamorphosis. A lobster's life cycle begins with a small, soft egg. Thousands of eggs stick to the bottom of the female lobster's tail until they hatch. When an egg hatches, the larva swims near the ocean's surface for a few weeks. As it grows, the larva sheds its exoskeleton many times. After some time, it sinks to the ocean floor where it lives for the rest of its life. As adult lobsters, the females can lay their own eggs, repeating the life cycle. Lobsters have a life span of about 50 years!

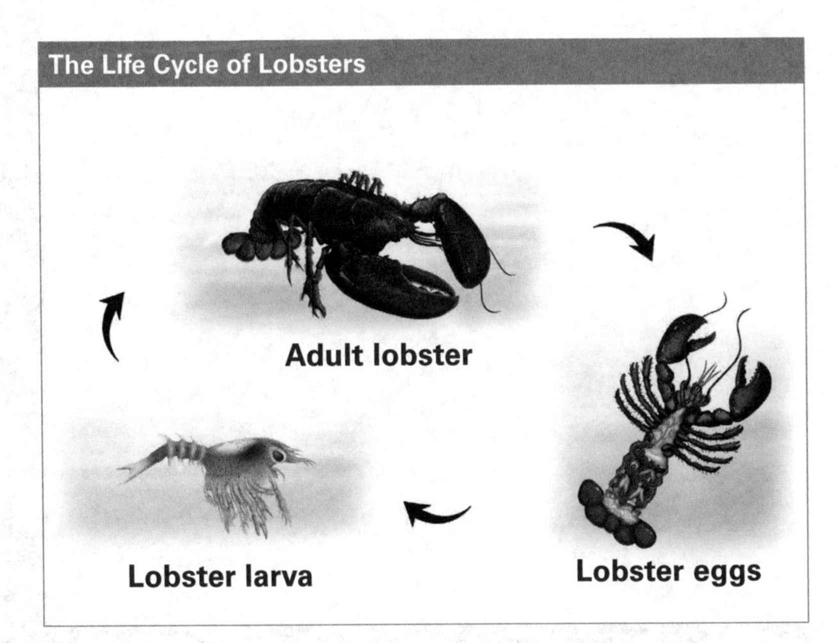

A lobster's life cycle has three stages. The eggs ride on the adult female's body. The larva molts many times before it becomes an adult.

Use this diagram to describe the lobster life cycle. Include these terms in your answer: **larva**, **eggs**, **adult**, and **exoskeleton**. Use sequence words, such as "first" and "next."

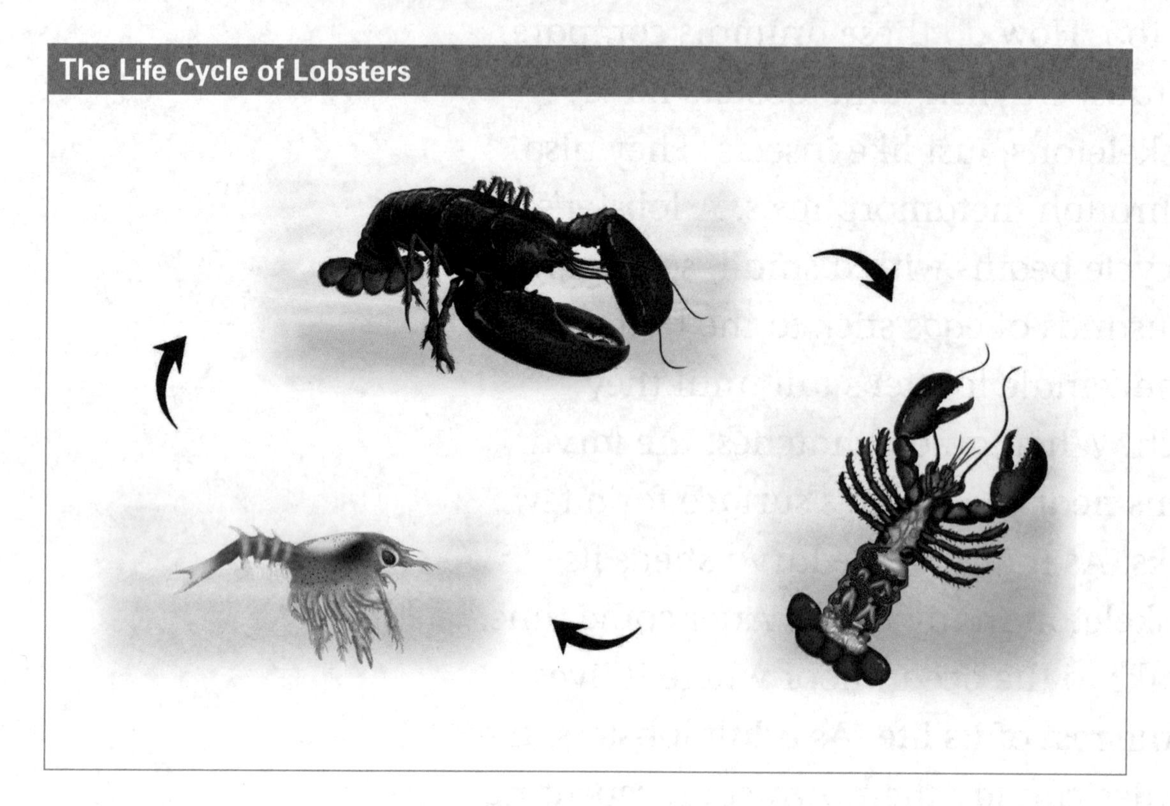

Show What You Know

You have learned about the life cycle models below. Scientists use what they already know to make predictions about what they do not know. Then they test their predictions.

Consider an organism you have not yet studied: moths. Moths are flying insects, closely related to butterflies, that are often active at nighttime. Based on this information, which of these life cycle diagrams do you think a moth's life cycle would be most similar to? Circle it.

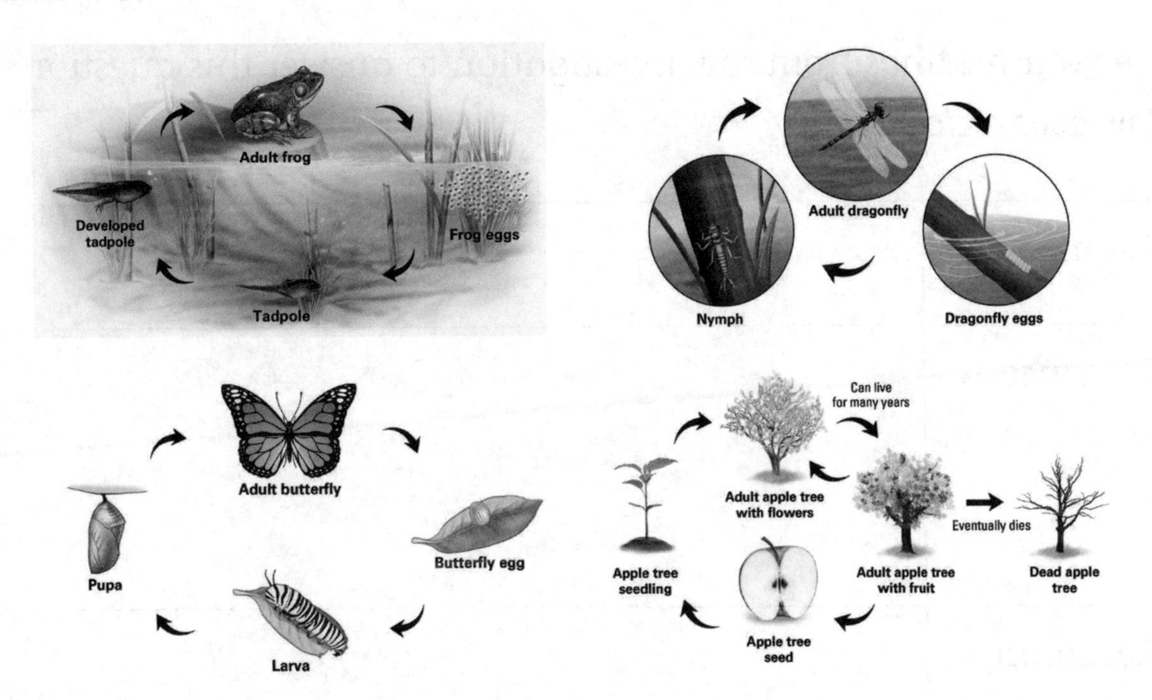

Research the life cycle of a moth online or in a book.
How is a moth's life cycle similar to the life cycle you chose above?

What differences do you see?

Making Sense of the Phenomenon

Let's revisit the phenomenon: *This cicada insect is leaving behind its old skin.*

Think about:

- Do other invertebrates have a similar hard body covering like this cicada?
- How are other invertebrates different?

Use your findings from the investigation to answer this question: *How does a cicada grow?*

Claim	
Evidence	
Reasoning	

☑ Go back to page 4 and fill out the unit checkpoint for this lesson.

NOTES

Performance Assessment:
Creating Infographics on Life Cycles

Develop infographics for Science Monthly to show the life cycles of different Ecuadorian plants and animals.

You will:

- collect data about the life cycles of different organisms.
- create an infographic that communicates information about the stages of a life cycle.
- compare life cycles, and use patterns to make predictions.

Learning About Life Cycles

Read the information in *Handout: Life Cycles*. Take notes on the life cycle of each plant or animal.

	Ecuador poison frog	**Frigatebird**	**Galápagos prickly pear**
Birth			
Growth			
Reproduction			
Death			

Brainstorming an Infographic

Assign each member of your group one organism. You will design an infographic that shows the life cycle of this organism.

An infographic is a way to show information and data using illustrations and symbols. It uses visuals, arrows, flowcharts, and text.

Which of the three organisms were you assigned?

Use the space below to plan an infographic that shows this organism's life cycle. Your infographic should have:

- a section for each stage of the organism's life cycle (birth, growth, reproduction, death).
- visuals that represent each stage in the organism's life cycle.
- captions that describe each life cycle stage and the relationships between each stage.
- arrows, flowcharts, or other symbols to show how the life cycle stages connect to one another.

Comparing Life Cycles

Share your infographic draft with your group members.

- Is the information accurate?
- Does the infographic clearly tell about the organism's life cycle?
- How can you improve the design?

Make corrections to your infographic.

Then, compare the life cycles of your group's organism to those of other groups. How are the life cycles similar? Write down patterns you notice.

How are the life cycles different?

Use patterns you see in the infographics to predict what will happen to these organisms if one of the life cycle stages were missing.

Question	Response
What would happen to these organisms if there were no more births?	
What would happen to these organisms if there was no more growth?	
What would happen to these organisms if there was no more reproduction?	
What would happen to these organisms if there was no more death?	

C

camouflage When an animal's color makes it hard to see against a similarly colored background.

E

environment All the living and nonliving things that surround an organism.

exoskeleton A hard body covering that protects soft inside parts of some animals.

F

flower A part of some plants where seeds are made.

fruit The part of a plant that surrounds and protects a seed.

G

genes Inherited information that tells offspring what traits to have.

I

inherited trait A characteristic passed from a parent to its offspring.

invertebrate An animal without a backbone, like insects, lobsters, and octopuses.

L

larva The second stage in the life cycle of some invertebrates. A larva becomes a pupa that goes through rapid metamorphosis.

learned behavior A trait an organism learns over its lifetime.

life cycle The pattern of changes that a member of a species goes through during its lifetime.

life span The typical amount of time that most members of a species live, from birth to death.

M

mate An animal that can reproduce with another animal of the same species.

metamorphosis A large change in body shape during the life cycle of some animal species.

N

nymph The second stage in the life cycle of many insects. These insects go through gradual metamorphosis.

O

offspring The young organisms that result when adult organisms reproduce.

R

reproduce To make more of the same species of an organism.

S

seed A small, protected part of a plant that can grow into an adult offspring.

species A group of living things of the same kind.

survive To stay alive.

T

trait A characteristic that a living thing has.

V

vertebrate An animal with a backbone.

Cover:
Els Jooren/Shutterstock

Title Page:
logoboom/iStockphoto

Unit Opener
2-3: imageBROKER / Alamy Stock Photo

Lesson 1

6: Countrymama/Dreamstime **7L:** Pond5 **7R:** Pond5 **8:** Thinkstock **9TL:** Thinkstock **9TC:** Thinkstock **9TR:** Alslutsky/Dreamstime **9C:** Fedorov Oleksiy **9BL:** Thinkstock **9BC:** fotofermer/iStockphoto **9BR:** Alslutsky/Dreamstime **11T:** Koi88/Dreamstime **11R:** Sean Pavone/Dreamstime **11L:** Nutthawit Wiangya/Dreamstime **12:** Steve Byland/Dreamstime **12:** Steve Byland/Dreamstime **12:** Ed Francissen/Dreamstime **12:** Joop Kleuskens/Dreamstime **12:** Bambi L. Dingman/Dreamstime **12:** Lochstampfer/Dreamstime **12:** South12th/Dreamstime **12:** Iuliia Skorupych/Dreamstime **12:** Maya Bunschoten/Dreamstime **12:** Ron Chapple/Dreamstime **12:** Ron Chapple/Dreamstime **12:** Ron Chapple/Dreamstime **12:** Paulpaladin/Dreamstime **12:** Antpkr/Dreamstime **12:** Nick M. Do/iStockphoto **12:** Bruce McIntosh/iStockphoto **12:** Alain/Dreamstime **12:** Amber Estabrooks/Dreamstime **12:** Howard Sandler/Dreamstime **12:** Brian Kushner/Dreamstime **13L:** Brian Kushner/Dreamstime **13R:** Brian Kushner/Dreamstime **14TL:** Nik Frey/Dreamstime **14TC:** Ruslan Kiyan/Dreamstime **14TR:** Aydindurdu/Dreamstime **14BL:** Mikhail Dudarev/Dreamstime **14BC:** Constantin Opris/Dreamstime **14BR:** Ivan Kmit/Dreamstime **15:** Len44ik/Dreamstime **16T:** Richardseeley/Dreamstime **16B:** 13claudio13/Dreamstime **17:** Szefei/Dreamstime **18T:** Wayne Mckown/Dreamstime **18BR:** fotofermer/iStockphoto **18BL:** beccarie/iStockphoto **19:** Isselee/Dreamstime **19:** Dan Breckwoldt/Dreamstime **19:** Beeldphoto/Dreamstime **19:** Erik Lam/Dreamstime **19:** Isselee/Dreamstime **19:** Eric Isselee/123rf **21T:** Photowitch/Dreamstime **21BL:** Thinkstock **21BCL:** Thinkstock **21BCR:** Thinkstock **21BR:** Nikolay Pozdeev/Dreamstime

Lesson 2

24: Byelikova/Dreamstime **25:** Pond5 **26:** Thinkstock **27:** Thinkstock **28:** Thinkstock **30:** Snicol24/Dreamstime **31T:** repistu/iStockphoto **31TC:** Ken Backer/Dreamstime **31BC:** Petr Mašek/Dreamstime **31B:** Allnaturalbeth/Dreamstime **32:** 12qwerty/Dreamstime **34:** Darrinhenry/Dreamstime **35:** Andrea Borsani/Dreamstime

Lesson 3

40: Heinz Effner/Dreamstime **41:** Pond5 **43:** Thinkstock **43:** Thinkstock **43:** Thinkstock **43:** Thinkstock **43:** Thinkstock **45L:** Anourina/Dreamstime **45R:** Milous Chab/Dreamstime **47B:** Romangorielov/Dreamstime **47T:** Thinkstock **49R:** Jolanta Dabrowska/Dreamstime **49L:** Audines/Dreamstime **50TR:** Jolanta Dabrowska/Dreamstime **50BR:** Audines/Dreamstime **50L:** Magnus Skjølberg/Dreamstime **51:** Lucy Cherniak/Dreamstime **52:** KeithBishop/iStockphoto **53T:** Thinkstock **53B:** Thinkstock

Lesson 4

56: Stuart G Porter/Shutterstock **57:** Pond5 **62:** Odm/Dreamstime **64:** Teodor Ostojic/Dreamstime **65:** Thinkstock **66:** Javarman/Dreamstime **68:** Egon Zitter/Dreamstime **69:** Thinkstock **70:** Fullempty/Dreamstime **72:** Derkien/Dreamstime **74T:** ThinkStock **74B:** Romastudio/Dreamstime

Performance Assessment

76: Ondřej Prosický | Dreamstime

Lesson 5

80: ValentynVolkov/iStockphoto **81:** Zdenek Sasek - Dreamstime.com **86:** Wam1975/Dreamstime **87:** Thinkstock **89:** Peter Vrabel/Dreamstime **93T:** Roman Samokhin/Dreamstime **93TCL:** Milosluz/Dreamstime **93TCR:** Vladitto/Shutterstock **93C:** Svetlana Mihailova/Dreamstime **93B:** archives/iStockphoto

Lesson 6

96: London Taxidermy/Alamy **97:** Pond5 **98T:** Natursports | Dreamstime **98TLC:** Thinkstock **98TRC:** Thinkstock **98TR:** Isselee | Dreamstime **98BL:** Krzysztof Odziomek | Dreamstime **98BLC:** Martyn Unsworth | Dreamstime **98BRC:** Xvaldes | Dreamstime **98BR:** Thinkstock **102:** Thinkstock **103:** Pp76/Dreamstime **103:** Humbak/Dreamstime **103:** Henrik Larsson/Shutterstock **103:** Chuyu/Dreamstime **103:** Eric Isselee/Shutterstock **104B:** Kheng Ho Toh/Dreamstime **104T:** Laschi/Dreamstime **106:** Eric Gevaert/Shutterstock **107:** Daburke/Dreamstime **108:** IrinaK/Shutterstock **109:** Jello5700/iStockphoto **109:** Daburke/Dreamstime **109:** IrinaK/Shutterstock **111:** Eric Isselee/Shutterstock **111:** Hintau Aliaksei/Shutterstock **111:** MoreenBlackthorne/Shutterstock **111:** Isselee/Dreamstime

Lesson 7

114: Mark Bridger/Shutterstock **115:** Shutterstock **119L:** Benjamin Simeneta/Dreamstime **119R:** Thinkstock **120L:** Brian Magnier/Dreamstime **120R:** Tonny Anwar/Dreamstime **122:** Amanda Melones/Dreamstime **124:** iliuta goean/Shutterstock **126T:** CharlesGibson/iStockphoto **126C:** Robert Pickett/Corbis **126B:** iliuta goean/Shutterstock

Performance Assessment

132: Pablo Hidalgo | Dreamstime